Grandma's Pet Wildebeest
Ate My Homework

(and other suspect stories)

A practical guide for parenting
and teaching ADHD kids

Tom Quinn
Licensed Professional Counselor
Dunvegan Publishing

Dunvegan Publishing
1170 Keystone Trail Drive
St. Louis, MO 63005

Library of Congress Catalog Card Number 98-92488
Manufactured in the United States of America
ISBN 0-9662590-0-9

Acknowledgments

There are so many people I need to thank for making this book a reality. My mother, May, and sister, Izzy, who put up with my ADHD for years and my wife, Lesa, and our two teenagers, Keith and Rachel.

Thanks to all my wonderful young ADHD clients and their families, past and present, who taught me so much.

Thanks to Karen, Sheryl, Nancy and Brett for being "test readers" and "devil's advocates."

Special thanks to Pam Kortum and Sheryl Silvey of the Learning Disabilities Association, St. Louis Affiliate, for their technical assistance and support.

Anna Ross, my patient editor, who learned fast how difficult it could be editing a manuscript written by an ADHD writer.

Special thanks also to Nancy Rice and Vince Schoemehl of CraftLink for their expertise, enthusiasm and willingness to go on a publishing adventure, Ed Drayton, the graphic designer, Dan, the production manager, Chris the PC Wizard and everyone else at CraftLink.

To Brett and Bob for their unflagging support and encouragement, and LaNelle, Darwin, Sheri, and Julie at the counseling office.

To Larry Runde, CPA, for his advice and encouragement.

To Ned Hallowell, and Sally Smith, who taught me so much through their writings and presentations.

Cover design: Ed Drayton
Cover illustration: Tom Quinn

Disclaimer

This book is designed to provide information in regard to the subject matter covered, namely ADHD. It is not designed to substitute the services of a competent, licensed clinician (psychiatrist, neurologist, pediatrician, psychologist, counselor, clinical social worker) in terms of assessment, diagnosis, treatment, or any other services rendered by such professionals.

Every effort has been made to make this guide as complete and accurate as possible. However, there may be mistakes typographically and from a content point of view. Based on this, the book should only be used as a guide and not the ultimate source of ADHD treatment. For that, you need the services of a clinician.

The examples and case studies all have been "fictionalized" for the sake of protecting the confidentiality and privacy of all clients, past and present. All names and recognizable personality characteristics have been changed and any references to individuals are coincidental.

DEDICATION

To my Dad,
the late Thomas McArdle Quinn,
who taught me to read and write.

Contents

Preface

This is the boring part, so read it quickly. I always skip introductions myself but I've learned that I'm required to have one for this book, so I'll make it as quick as possible.

Okay, so why another book about Attention Deficit Hyperactivity Disorder (ADHD, or even ADD, as they're both called the same thing nowadays)? What makes this one different from any of the others that are currently available?

There are several reasons. The first is that this book focuses more on practical tips and techniques on how to manage ADHD, a how-to manual for parents and educators dealing with kids who have ADHD. Of course, there are many wonderful academic and theoretical books currently available on ADHD, but this isn't one of them.

Secondly, I've not only written from the point of view of a counselor who specializes in the treatment of ADHD but also from a personal point of view, as I'm an ADHD adult myself.

Finally, I make use of humor as most of my clients are standing on their last nerve, thanks to all those years of living with a basket case kid. Humor lightens the load, and offers some hope that having an ADHD kid needn't be the end of the world.

To be honest, it's taken quite a while to actually write this book. Although I'm the editor and publisher of the *St. Louis ADD Newsletter*, the thought of having to be structured and organized enough to complete a non-fiction book was quite daunting. In the past several years, I've written three novels (none of which were published), numerous short stories (some of which were *almost* published), and some poetry (all of which I pray never will be published), but this is my first non-fiction book. At least, most of it's non-fiction. (I took some liberties here and there to illustrate certain key points.)

Watching my frustration grow as a writer, my family, friends, and colleagues suggested that perhaps all my writing instructors had a point when they told me to "Write what you know." So now I'm writing what I know, namely kids with ADHD.

I hope this book will be of some help to you, your children, or someone you care about.

Tom Quinn,
St. Louis, Missouri
March, 1998

Chapter 1

ADHD: That Child Ain't Right

If ever there was a condition that has been misunderstood, ADHD is one of them. It's been called Minimal Brain Dysfunction, Hyperkinetic Syndrome, ADD, and ADHD, to name a few of the more recent labels. I'm sure there will be other names in the future which sound more pleasing to the ear, like Really-Creative-But-Doesn't-Like-Structure-Disorder or Really-Nice-Kid-But-a-Pain-to-Live-With-Disorder but for the moment, we're stuck with ADHD.

Deciding exactly what ADHD is and what it isn't has been one of the ongoing debates in the psychology world, causing heated arguments not only in academia but also in the media. Rush Limbaugh even jumped into the fray several years ago claiming there's no such thing as ADHD, fueling the flames of controversy even further.

But let's assume Mr. Limbaugh was a little too hasty in his proclamation, and examine the subject for ourselves, beginning with the fact that we live in an ADHD-like culture, an observation wonderfully exemplified several years ago by a cable TV show on Comedy Central called "Short Attention Span Theater." Instead of having to sit through a whole thirty minutes of a comedy show, we were exposed to only *one scene* from a show, rapidly followed by scenes from other comedy shows.

We also live in a fast-paced, hyper type of society— have a headache? Take Excedrin. Learn guitar in two days! Overweight? Lose 300 pounds overnight by taking New Improved Fataway Tablets! Feel nervous? Pop a Xanex! Got ADHD? Here, have a Ritalin or try these new exciting Blue-Green Algae pills which are currently being touted as a treatment for ADHD. (Where do you get this stuff, anyway—scrape the inside of your kid's fish tank?)

We now speak in sound bytes instead of sentences. TV commercials cram so many visual and auditory stimuli into a thirty-second time slot you can develop instant ADHD. And don't get me started on dizzying TV commercials by used car dealers or mad carpet salesmen, you know, those guys in loud, plaid blazers with buzz-cuts or slicked-down hair who scream at you on Friday evenings, the cameras zooming in and out while they yell, "Boy, do I have a deal for you down at Billy Bob's Used Car Lot and Rugs!"

You get the idea. As you can see, we live in an attention-grabbing, impulse-spending culture, the results of which can be high distractibility, short attention span, restlessness, and jitteriness. Funnily enough, these are also major symptoms of ADHD.

So are we dealing with the side effects of our loony culture or are we dealing with a true neurological condition? In other words, we need to define exactly what we mean by ADHD, the Disorder Formerly Known As ADD.

First of all, we have to be careful we don't pathologize normal child and adolescent behavior. Our society is very good at labeling and making syndromes out of any number of human behaviors, and ADHD is no exception.

As a clinician, I spend some of my time *un*diagnosing ADHD kids who were incorrectly labeled and categorized after a ten-minute evaluation by some quack. They've been medicated ever since just because they were a little rambunctious or fidgety!

So what *is* the difference between ADHD behavior and typical child and adolescent behavior? Many kids are distractible, rowdy, and don't like doing homework, but this doesn't mean they have ADHD. But children who have all these symptoms over an extended time period in such a way that they interfere with their lives, well, that's probably more than just typical kid stuff, possibly ADHD. So let's take a look at the official signs and symptoms to find out what we're dealing with.

Attention Deficit Hyperactivity Disorder comes in four varieties, the first three being the most prevalent:

ADHD: Hyperactive-Impulsive Type (HIT)
ADHD: Predominantly Inattentive Type (PIT)
ADHD: Combined Type (CT)
ADHD: Not Otherwise Specified (NOS)

The symptoms are listed in the manual of psychiatric disorders that all clinicians use to make a diagnosis, the *Diagnostic and Statistical Manual of Mental Disorders, Fourth Edition*, the DSM-IV.

The DSM-IV lists the diagnostic criteria for Attention Deficit/Hyperactivity Disorder as follows:

A. Either (1) or (2)

   (1) six (or more) of the following symptoms of *inattention* have persisted for at least six months to a degree

that is maladaptive and inconsistent with developmental level:

Inattention

(a) often fails to give close attention to details or makes careless mistakes in school work, work, or other activities
(b) often has difficulty sustaining attention in tasks or play activities
(c) often does not seem to listen when spoken to directly
(d) often does not follow through on instructions and fails to finish schoolwork, chores, or duties in the workplace (not due to oppositional behavior or failure to understand instructions)
(e) often has difficulty organizing tasks and activities
(f) often avoids, dislikes, or is reluctant to engage in tasks that require sustained mental effort (such as schoolwork or homework)
(g) often loses things necessary for tasks or activities (e.g. toys, school assignments, pencils, books, or tools)
(h) is often easily distracted by extraneous stimuli
(i) is often forgetful in daily activities

(2) six (or more) of the following symptoms of *hyperactivity-impulsivity* have persisted for at least six months to a degree that is maladaptive and inconsistent with developmental level:

Hyperactivity

(a) often fidgets with hands or feet or squirms in seat
(b) often leaves seat in classroom or in other situations in which remaining seated is expected
(c) often runs about or climbs excessively in situations in which it is inappropriate (in adolescents or adults, may be limited to subjective feelings of restlessness)
(d) often has difficulty playing or engaging in leisure activities quietly
(e) is often "one the go" or often acts as if "driven by a motor"
(f) often talks excessively

Impulsivity

(g) often blurts out answers before questions have been completed
(h) often has difficulty awaiting turn
(i) often interrupts or intrudes on others (e.g. butts into conversations or games)

B. Some hyperactive-impulsive or inattentive symptoms that caused impairment were present before age seven.

C. Some impairment from the symptoms is present in two or more settings (e.g. at school or work and at home).

D. There must be clear evidence of clinically significant impairment in social, academic or occupational functioning.

E. The symptoms do not occur exclusively during the courses of a Pervasive Developmental Disorder, Schizophrenia, or other Psychotic Disorder and are not better accounted for by another mental disorder (e.g. Mood Disorder, Anxiety Disorder, Dissociative Disorder, or a Personality Disorder).

Although this is the official word on diagnosis from the clinician's perspective, using the DSM-IV, we can reduce the technical detail and jargon to a more simplified form, and define ADHD as *a neurological, biological condition with a pattern of restlessness, impulsivity, and distractibility which disrupts family life, school work, and social skills to the extent that they interfere with daily living.*

Using this definition, we'll now examine each category of ADHD—HIT (Hyperactive-Impulsive Type), PIT (Predominantly Inattentive Type), CT (Combined Type), and NOS (Not Otherwise Specified) from a more hands-on perspective.

1. ADHD: Hyperactive-Impulsive Type (HIT)

This is the type most people are familiar with, the hyper kid who drives everyone crazy, the one who doesn't know how to shut his big mouth, who ties up his sister and locks her in the hope chest, who is easily excited, and generally creates chaos wherever and whenever the mood strikes him. I use the pronoun "he" because boys are better than girls. Oops! Sorry, no, they're not, the reason is because we see this type more in boys. Really. It's true.

Not only does he receive negative attention from parents, teachers, and even other kids, but in some cases, he actually seems to thrive on it. He becomes bored so easily that while picking a fight with Mom or Dad might result in grounding or creates some other consequence, it can also be exciting and even energizing. The conflict creates an adrenaline rush, which in a bizarre fashion, appears to focus his wandering attention, and well, to him, it just seems like a good idea at the time. And you may also notice that when you tell him he's grounded, not only does he not seem to care, he really doesn't!

This is the kid who constantly finds himself in all sorts of trouble without even realizing what he's done half the time. How often have you confronted your kid for doing something wrong and he swears he has no idea what you're talking about, like an alien took over his mind and body. At the time, it really did seem like a fine idea, but with no thought, none, into any future consequences, and then, *POW!* he's nailed.

Does this type of scenario sound familiar—?

You: "Did you chop the heads off all the daffodils in the front yard?"
Him: "I don't know what you're talking about."
You: "Oh, sure! You're grounded!"
Him: "But I didn't *do* anything!"
You: "Grounded for one week."
Him: "I don't care!"
You: "Fine! Two weeks."
Him: "Why don't you make it three!"

And all the while you and he are arguing, he's playing with a Bic cigarette lighter, rubber ball, picking lint off his pants, staring out the window, walking around in circles and muttering under his breath about what a jerk you are.

See why we call this Hyperactive-Impulsive?

But can you both let it go at this? Oh, no, we have to keep going!

> *You:* "What were you *thinking?*"
> *Him:* "Huh? I dunno."
> (And you want to scream because if he's a teenager, that's the only answer you ever get to a direct question.)
> *You:* "What do you mean, you don't know?"
> *Him:* Shoulder shrug, followed by indiscernible mumbling.
> *You:* "How can you not know, for crying out loud! They didn't chop off their own heads!"

On and on into that deep dark night . . . But you know, he might be telling you the truth; he *wasn't* thinking. He just had this wild idea about beheading flowers and ran with it, carried away in the heat of the moment. So where did this beheading idea come from, anyway? It turns out he'd been half-listening to a TV documentary on PBS about *The Mikado*, a Victorian operetta by Gilbert and Sullivan, and the part about Ko-Ko, the Lord High Executioner, caught his attention for a few moments, then he went outside to play in the yard. He saw the daffodils and all their little yellow heads just *pleading* to be lopped off as if *he* were the Lord High Executioner, which when he thought about it, sounded like a really cool job, and then. . .

Now, a word of caution, this is an explanation for *why* he chopped off the daffodil heads, *not* an excuse for his behavior. ADHD should never be used as an excuse otherwise there is no accountability or responsibility, two important traits you've probably been trying to get through his head for the last ten years.

You see why you feel like tearing your hair out in frustration?

Think of this exchange as a kind of dance. You both know the steps, the familiar music starts playing, and you both waltz into the foray, the conflict escalating, accompanied by yelling and tears with neither of you getting anywhere.

Are there any alternatives?

Sure there are, but they aren't easy or quick. Learning new ways of parenting an ADHD kid requires bucketloads of patience and persistence on your part. Clear thinking is vital. When conflict arises, try to step back and think it through before taking any action.

Solutions for Clear Thinking

1. *What's the situation?*

    Junior did something impulsive/thoughtless, unheeding of the consequences.

2. *What does he need?*

    The instinctive answer is a kick in the rear, but it's the wrong answer. He needs to learn how to interrupt his own impulsive train of thought and to understand potential consequences *before* taking any action.

3. *What do you need?*

> Valium. Lots of it. And a way to get through to Mr.
> Blockhead standing here. And honesty, you need him
> to be honest because the odds are high he's pretty
> quick to tell lies.

4. *Options: Yelling, screaming, berating, shaming, beating?*

> Nope, because they don't work, not in the long term.
> If you do yell, he'll simply tune you out *but* pretend
> he's listening. He learned that one by about age five.

Educate him? Absolutely! If the bottom line is you want to teach him not to do mindless things, you have to educate him. How? Repetition, repetition, repetition, over and over. And over. Education along with consequences? Most definitely. This is one of the hardest concepts to get across to an ADHD kid, that there really is such a thing as cause and effect.

But with consistency and persistence, you can avoid escalating the conflict and even start getting through to him that cause and effect is a reality.

However, if you're not consistent, forget it. Being inconsistent tells him you're not taking the situation seriously, so why should he?

By the way, grounding him for twenty years probably won't cut it either. Try a day or so. Even better, send him to visit Great Aunt Ethel for a couple of days, your mother's sister who lives three states away.

2. ADHD: Predominantly Inattentive Type (PIT)

Until fairly recently, this type had been dubbed "Female ADD" as we saw it more in girls than in boys, mainly because we'd gotten so used to the in-your-face HIT symptoms in boys. However, we're beginning to realize that boys also can suffer from the Predominantly Inattentive Type. The PIT is much more subtle, less obvious, and easily missed.

If your child has this type, what in the old days we called ADD, he or she may have been called names like "Space Cadet," "Dreamer," "Head in the Clouds," (or in my own case, "Him Living in Cloud Cuckoo Land," which was my grandfather's nickname for me). This is the kid who lives in his own world, the dreamer, the romantic, and the poet, the Steven Spielberg of the mind.

Although she shares the same low tolerance for routine and boredom as her hyper counterpart, the PIT's method of alleviating this boredom is vastly different. Instead of raising hell like Hyper Harry, the Dreamy Diana PIT hitches a ride on the tail of a golden comet, and arcs across the dark velvet sky of Never-Never Land to create a whole new daydreaming reality for herself.

Initially, the PIT may be difficult to identify for the following reasons:

a) she usually doesn't cause too much of a ruckus and draw negative attention to herself

b) she may have learned to *look as if* she's paying attention even though her mind is miles away

For the first couple of years of school, and especially because she's so quiet, no one really pays much attention to her daydreaming and distractibility, but around sixth or seventh grade, academic problems begin to materialize from the increasing workload and demands of school.

To complicate matters further, if we as parents and teachers have stereotypical notions of ADHD, this may prevent early detection and intervention. As long as we're not seeing hyperactivity or impulsivity, we assume we're not dealing with ADHD, a dangerous assumption.

Here are a couple of comments I've heard over the years about PITs which demonstrate the dangers of stereotyping ADHD:

> "She's too sweet to have ADD."
> "He's no trouble in class."
> "She always has a smile." (Of course she does—she
> uses that smile to get you off her back!)
> "He never causes a fuss." (Why would he, he's too busy
> watching all those movies playing inside his head!)
> "She flunked that last test but I gave her a passing grade
> because she's such a sweet kid." (Yeah? What kind of
> message does that give her—be cute and sweet and the
> world will take care of you?)

And while every parent enjoys hearing "nice" things being said about their child, what about the fact that she's in fifth grade but reads and writes like a third grader? Oh, but that's okay because she's cute and she'll catch up? I think not! She doesn't pay attention, falls behind in her work, but covers it up by being "nice." Meanwhile, her self-esteem is plummeting because she's no dummy—she knows she's falling behind her classmates even though she can't figure out why. Her only conclusion is that she must be dumb after all.

By seventh grade, she's a Maven of Cuteness, using deception and sweetness to survive. But at what cost? By eighth grade, the other kids know about her tendency to "zone out," and now she has to contend with being called an "airhead" or a "space cadet," doing further damage to her already-fragile self-esteem.

This zoning out is a red flag in terms of identifying ADHD PIT. Sure, all of us have moments when we space out, what we call dissociative states; you're driving down the highway but can't remember the last two miles you just traveled or you're simply daydreaming, staring out the window for a few seconds. But PIT zoning can be constant, clicking in and out hundreds, maybe thousands of times each day.

Another classic PIT symptom is distractibility. Have you ever asked your kid to pick up his book bag from the front door, collect his shoes, and put all of them in his room? Then you say, "Oh, and on the way past the bathroom, hang up the towels you left there this morning. How many times do I have to tell you to hang up those towels!"

He stares at you with that oh-so-familiar vacant look, then grunts at you reassuringly. Ten minutes later, you enter the hall. There's the book bag still lying on the floor. The shoes are there, too. The towels litter the bathroom floor like dead wet dogs. There's no sign of him anywhere until you hear the beep of a computer game. You march into the den and find him lying sprawled on the floor playing *Cyber Death Nazis Nuke A Cute Purple Dinosaur*.

You tower over him, hands on hips and ask, "What do you think you're playing at, young man?"

And he looks up at you like you're nuts, with a facial expression that says, "What do you think I'm doing; it's a computer game, you moron!"

He doesn't have the slightest idea why you're angry, either. The book bag, shoes, and bathroom towels? Are you serious? That was *way* back in the past, over ten whole minutes ago. He made it as far as the hall, picked up one of the shoes but suddenly noticed the sole was shaped like one of the Death Carver Laser guns in the computer game. He turned his head around, saw the computer *begging* to be switched on and the next minute, he was on the Planet Zoobedorg fighting Cyber Death Nazis, and here you are worried about towels and a stupid book bag?

Zoning out and distractibility are classic PIT symptoms. Here are some more PIT symptoms not listed in the DSM-IV but could be:

- Easily bored, and I mean *easily*
- Has the attention span of a gnat
- Latches onto a hobby or interest to the point of becoming obsessed, then suddenly quits to begin a new hobby
- Tunes you out like you don't exist on a regular basis
- Stubborn as a mule
- Has a hard time following through with routines
- Has an ability to "hyperfocus"
- Tells lies and tall tales better than Mark Twain
- Frequently appears comatose or dead
- Doesn't seem to understand English

As a parent, you spend most of your waking hours and even some of your sleeping hours worrying what will become of this kid. Will he make it? How on earth will he survive?

Will he ever get through high school, what with his homework allergy and all?

You feel guilty because you must have done something wrong somewhere along the line. You feel guilty because you're always nagging him—"Hang up those towels." "Where's your homework?" "Where's your book bag?" "Turn out those lights." "Put the dishes in the dishwasher, don't just leave them in the sink, for crying out loud!"

On and on, like the Nagging Mom From Hell (NMFH). Hounding him, berating him, but yet he's such a good sweet kid and you really do feel like the NMFH when he gives you that hurt look. . .

But as he becomes older, he mouths off to you more often and louder, his temper is getting shorter, and the fighting and arguing increase. You're stressed, he's stressed, the whole family is in constant turmoil, and you wonder whatever happened to that sweet little kid you used to know.

Okay, so what can you do about ADHD PIT?

Solutions

1. Learn everything you can about ADHD PIT to see if this really is what your kid is suffering from. If you suspect he is, schedule an evaluation with a competent professional.

2. Quit taking everything so personally (easier said than done). He's probably not being a space cadet just to annoy you (although in some cases, he might be).

3. If he does have ADHD PIT, accept the fact that you're dealing with a kid who has a biological, neurological con-

dition which may explain some of what he does in a context other than just trying to tick you off.

4. Make your expectations more realistic. A common expectation is that if you tell him to do something, he should listen (ha ha) but he doesn't. Instead of punishing him for having ADHD, you and he need to learn how to *manage* the ADHD, all of which will be explained in the following chapters.

5. Teach him directly how his ADHD causes many of these problems. Show him how to start managing his life more effectively. And yes, this does require heroic patience and understanding, but it sure beats the constant nagging, yelling, arguing, and dealing with all the sneaky, little passive-aggressive ways he tries to get back at you.

If zoning out is the hallmark of ADHD PIT, and hyperactivity-impulsivity is ADHD HIT, what does it mean if you see both? Probably ADHD, Combined Type (CT).

3. ADHD: Combined Type (CT)

This type is simple to describe; take the HIT and the PIT, combine them, and voilá, you have ADHD Combined Type, (CT), the best (or worst) of both types.

ADHD CT is when you have this quiet, daydreaming kid, who for no apparent reason can turn psycho, suddenly becomes hyperactive, and stymies everyone who knows him. Or he can be predominantly hyperactive but then displays moments/hours/days when everything is calm, lulling you into a false sense of security, until *WHAM!* the hyperactivity kicks into high gear again, 0-60 mph in nanoseconds.

Another variation is the predominantly daydreaming kid, who, while not exactly hyper, can't stop fidgeting, squirms in his chair, moves constantly, taps his pen on the desk, drums his fingers, taps his feet, and drives everyone crazy, oblivious as to how much he's irritating everyone around him (I *still* do this on occasion).

One of the dangers of having a child with the Combined Type is in setting him up for a double bind. When you see the hyperactivity, you yell at him to knock it off, but in doing so, you're merely reinforcing his inattentive tendencies—he only feels acceptable when he's in his inattentive mode. The trouble is that you now start confronting him for being a daydreamer and a space cadet. Pretty soon, you have a kid on your hands who feels as if he's in a "damned if I do, damned if I don't" scenario, which adds to his stress, low self-esteem, and confusion.

The same principles from the other two types, HIT and PIT, apply here—educate, educate, educate—yourself, your child, family members, and teachers.

You know how it feels to have an ADHD child, but for a moment, put yourself in his or her shoes (if you can find them).

During a recent counseling session, the mother of twelve-year-old Billy explained how difficult her life was raising him, while Billy sat beside her, tapping his feet and looking out the window, seemingly oblivious to what she was saying.

"Have you any idea what I go through?" she asked. "Do you know what it feels like to have him go hyper all of a sudden, doing really dumb things, acting without any thought to the consequences, always in trouble with his teachers, always tapping his feet and fidgeting like he's got ants in his pants?"

Before I could reply, Billy leaned forward, and glared at both of us. His voice was quiet for once.

"Do you guys have any idea what *I* go through when that happens? Do you ever think about how it feels when your mouth opens all by itself and really dumb stuff comes out and you make a fool of yourself and you get detention and the other kids laugh at you and you get sent to the principal and your mom and dad think you're a jerk even though you promised yourself you wouldn't do anything dumb today? For the millionth time?"

Mom didn't know what to say, because the truth was, she never really had considered it from his point of view.

One of Billy's biggest problems, like he said, was his mouth. A component of *all* the ADHD types is a lowered inhibition, which often shows up via a big mouth.

When you were a child, how many times did you think, "I wish that stupid teacher would shut her mouth." Of course, you'd never dream of actually saying the words because you had an editor inside your head whose job it was to silence you before you made these thoughts into speech.

In many ADHD kids, the editor is half-dead or asleep most of the time, so that when the thought arises, "Shut up, you stupid jerk!" the editor doesn't catch it, and the thoughts come rushing out in a torrent of words before the kid realizes what's happening. Now he's facing *another* detention, and the cycle continues.

Instead of the internal process being "Ready, Aim, Fire!" the mouthy ADHD kid's is "Ready, Fire, Aim!"

Solutions

1. Explain the concept of the Internal Editor to your child.

2. Have him draw a picture of himself with a zipper or padlock on his mouth, explaining that this is what the editor looks like.

3. Teach him that every time an insulting or negative thought arises, he has to grab the zipper and shut it or slam down the latch on the padlock, providing him with a more graphic frame of reference.

4. An alternative is for him to wear a rubber band on his wrist and every time a mouthy thought arises, he has to *quietly* snap the band on his wrist to interrupt the mouthing-off process, giving the editor a chance to wake up. A word of caution—for some kids, putting a rubber band on their wrists is an invitation to fire it at other kids or snap it repeatedly, in which case we've just set him up. Everything depends on the individual child.

Having read about the first three types, you may have recognized some of your child's behavior. But what happens if you see your kid in some of these descriptions, yet his behavior doesn't quite fit all of the diagnostic criteria? In that case, we have to consider the fourth type, ADHD NOS.

4. ADHD: Not Otherwise Specified (NOS)

NOS is a diagnostic catch-all for those ADHD behaviors which don't fall exactly into the traditional diagnostic criteria. As clinicians, we may have a good idea that we're dealing with ADHD but yet there are some anomalies that don't quite fit our convenient symptom lists. The NOS diagnosis is useful because the reality of the human condition is that while *many* or *most* kids fit the diagnostic criteria, there are always exceptions, a testament to our uniqueness as human beings.

Conclusion

So as you can see, ADHD is not simply a case of being hyper, talking too much, or zoning out. Within the umbrella of ADHD are four separate variations, all of which contain their own unique characteristics, and even then, each kid has his or her own cluster of symptoms which may differ slightly from another kid's. That's why working with a knowledgeable professional is important.

There are other signs and symptoms not listed in the "official" diagnostic criteria or in more scholarly works, symptoms seen often enough by parents and teachers to warrant further investigation. You observe definite patterns of behavior, and although you think they might be signs of ADHD, when you look in all the books, there's not too much mention of them.

These behavior patterns are explained in the following chapter, *Other Stuff Parents See But Can't Quite Figure Out.*

Chapter 2

Other Stuff Parents See But Can't Quite Figure Out: The Unofficial Symptoms

These "unofficial" symptoms may not be specifically mentioned in the research literature, but even so, parents, therapists in the ADHD field, and the kids themselves, frequently report them.

These signs and symptoms include *playing with fire, an addiction to Mountain Dew, frequent lying, having to spell out details* exactly, *obsessive thinking, and fidgeting* (also an official symptom).

Unofficial Symptom #1: Playing with Fire

Many boys, ADHD or not, go through periods in which they like to burn things. Nevertheless, there appears to be a high proportion of ADHD boys who have a definite fascination with fire, like moths to a flame. I can't recall a single ADHD teenager I've worked with who didn't carry a lighter in his pocket. Now, before you start freaking out because your kid does that, I'm not talking about him being a junior arsonist or pyromaniac, so just relax. I'm referring to a pattern of behavior that involves being visually entranced by flickering light.

A case in point is fifteen-year-old David. During a family counseling session, I asked if he had a lighter in his possession.

"I don't smoke," he said.

"I didn't ask if you smoked. I asked if you had a lighter."

With great reluctance, David produced a red plastic Bic, much to the surprise of his parents.

I continued, "You like to melt plastic straws?"

He nodded.

"GI Joes and other little plastic guys?"

"Uh-huh."

"Candles?"

"Light them all the time."

"But it's not that you're a budding pyromaniac or a junior terrorist; you just love watching the flame and the really cool designs which form from the gobs of melting plastic, right?"

"Yes!" he said, relieved that someone finally understood.

Dad frowned at me. "What are you two going on about?"

I explained my theory, that the flame seems to grab the attention of ADHD kids in the same manner of a Nintendo or the flickering of a computer monitor. The flickering seems to produce a form of optical stimulation that kicks up the metabolic speed of the brain just like the action of Ritalin or other stimulants, which then puts the kid into a "hyperfocus" mode. Hence, the fascination with fire and computers. At least, that's my theory.

I've discussed this phenomenon with a couple of other therapists in the ADHD field who've made similar observations, and although we can't count this as a true symptom per se, we believe there may be a connection.

If this is true (I'll leave this one to the researchers) does that mean that one day we can attach computer monitors to the heads of ADHD kids and zap them with timed bursts of flickering light instead of using medication?

I have no idea, but I'll be interested to see if there are any future developments in this area.

Meanwhile, next time your kid is hyper, just stick him in front of a Nintendo. That should take care of him for a little while. . .

Unofficial Symptom #2: Addicted to Mountain Dew

I know this sounds bizarre, but there's not an ADHD kid I know who doesn't consume vast quantities of this soft drink. The first time I heard about the ADHD-Mountain Dew connection was several years ago from the mother of an ADHD kid who said that her pediatrician had told her Mountain Dew would help calm down her hyper son. She tried it, and amazingly, the kid stopped being hyper for about half an hour, flying in the face of conventional wisdom about not giving sugar to kids because it makes them hyper.

Over the years, I've discussed this with Dew-guzzling teenagers, all of whom have said not only does it help calm them, but even produces a general sense of well-being. Some even claim it helps them study!

There may be a grain of truth here, in that Mountain Dew contains one of the highest levels of caffeine among soft drinks as well as a relatively high level of sugar. Given that, I suspect the combination mimics the action of stimulant medication, speeding up the glucose-burn in the ADHD brain, a result of which is a lessening of certain symptoms (more about this later).

I always wondered why Mountain Dew was my favorite soft drink. Now I know. So if your kid stockpiles cases of Mountain Dew, think of it more as an attempt at self-medication instead of trying to find a cheap sugar-high!

Unofficial Symptom #3: Lying

> *"O, what a tangled web we weave,*
> *When first we practise to deceive!"*

—Sir Walter Scott (1771-1832), Scottish novelist.

If there was ever a cross-section of the population who've raised lying to the level of a fine art, it's the ADHD kids. Telling tall tales and other suspect stories, these guys are true masters.

That's not to say that only ADHD kids lie; many kids lie to some extent, but the ADHD ones really know how to take it to extremes.

Lying is one of the more common complaints I hear about from parents (their kids lying, I mean). Some of these kids are so good that no matter how outrageous their stories are, you find yourself actually believing them (except for the one about Grandma's homework-eating wildebeest, a story created by a kid who was tired of being disbelieved any time he claimed the dog ate his homework!).

On one of my bookshelves at the office, there is a book about fiction writing by the famous mystery writer, Lawrence Block, entitled *Telling Lies for Fun and Profit.* As soon as I show a copy to any ADHD kid, his eyes light up with excitement. Instead of being in trouble for lying, this author guy gets paid vast sums of money! Such a deal!

Why do ADHD kids lie so much anyway?

1. Covering up mistakes
2. Strong imagination but no focus or outlet
3. Protecting a tattered self-esteem
4. Boredom

No. 1 Reason for Lying: Covering up Mistakes

After so many years of being in trouble, and now fully established as family scapegoats, ADHD kids often lie as a way to cover for themselves. They're so tired of being in trouble, so tired of being told they've screwed up yet again, they simply lie. Early on, they discover that lying sometimes gets them off the hook; eventually, lying becomes a knee-jerk response to confrontation and an attempt to provide breathing space for themselves between confrontations. If they didn't lie, and were punished *every* single time they did something wrong, they'd have complete nervous breakdowns (so would you, for that matter, so don't be sitting there all sanctimonious about how *you* never lied when you were a kid!). What they have a hard time grasping is how self-defeating and destructive their lying has become.

I remember one unfortunate scapegoat kid I worked with, Rick, who had a terrible habit of lying. He told me up-front that he knew he lied to cover his tracks. Reluctantly, he then admitted that this technique wasn't working too well because he was invariably caught, and he ended up being punished twice—once for the infraction of rules and a second time for lying about it.

Deciding it was time to grow up (with a little "encouragement" from Mom and Dad), he resolved to quit lying so much, a task which he soon discovered sounded much easier than it actually was.

One of the first strategies I used with Rick was to ask him to write down every time he lied each day, a technique I'd successfully used in the past with other kids. After a week of recording lies, Rick was shocked that the number ran into the hundreds, a realization that spurred him further on his new quest for honesty.

But after a promising start, he ran into trouble. One night he was hanging out with some friends who decided to get up to mischief. Rick declined to take part, wishing to prove to himself, his parents, and me that he was no longer the family scapegoat.

His friends, surprised and disappointed by this new behavior, called him a wuss and a dork, and did their best to persuade him to join in. Nevertheless, Rick resisted the overwhelming urge to participate, and instead, simply stood by to watch. Then, just as he'd feared would happen, they were caught.

At this point, you'd think Rick would have been relieved to be out of the firing line, and that would have been the end of it, but the story took a peculiar twist—Rick took all the blame!

When he told me, I was puzzled. "Why on earth did you do that?" I asked.

"Look, I'm the scapegoat. I'm the one who's always behind any trouble, and tee-peeing and egging a house is just the kind of garbage I get involved in. If I'd told my parents I had nothing to do with it, you think they'd buy that?"

Good point. There was no way they'd believe him. "I guess not," I said.

"Right. So if I'd denied it, not only would they have punished me for egging Chad's house, they'd have punished me even more for lying to them."

I was amazed. He was telling me that he lied about doing something he didn't even *do* so that he wouldn't diminish the parental trust he was working so hard to earn.

"That's crazy!" I said.

"I know," he said, a defeated tone in his voice. "So why even bother telling the truth if it only gets you in trouble?"

I saw his point, but Rick had to learn that the only way out of trouble was to tell the truth, no matter what. Hesitantly, he agreed to participate in a family conference during which he explained to his parents what had really happened that night. Initially, they were suspicious—how could they not be? —but by the end of the conference, they gradually began to understand Rick's strange predicament.

During the conference, Rick came to grasp how much his lying in the past had cost him. He'd thought all he had to do was start being honest, and that would change everything, but now he realized that re-establishing credibility was going to take considerable time and effort.

Finally, he learned that it was better not to engage in scapegoat behavior in the first place, as this eliminated any need to tell cover up lies!

No. 2 Reason for Lying: Overactive Imagination

Many ADHD kids are highly creative, and with their "overactive" imaginations, they become natural-born story-tellers. The downside is they usually have such a desperate need for an audience, along with an inability to focus their story telling, that pretty soon they can't distinguish fact from fiction. An embellishment here, an exaggeration there, throw in a low tolerance for boredom, and the tall tales become second nature.

By the time your average ADHD kid is in his early teens, storytelling has become part of who he is.

Instead of trying to eradicate this trait, we try to channel it. One creative technique is to have him write stories, using the title of Lawrence Block's book to get the point across that novelists are liars too, only they don't tell lies in ways that will create problems. Instead, they even get their faces on the cover of *People* magazine because they've told better lies than other paid liars!

ADHD kids with overactive imaginations *love* this concept. A few with whom I worked several years ago are now majoring in English, and one guy is in the MFA (Master of Fine Arts) program at a prestigious university. Not bad for a kid who used to be a little liar face!

The goal is not to extinguish the wonderful creativity, but to transform it using a technique we call "reframing." That means taking a given phenomenon (in this case, lying), and looking at it from a different perspective. Instead of saying, "You're nothing but a wee liar face," you reframe the concept by saying, "Hey, I notice you're pretty good at telling stories. Do you realize what a talent this is? Tell you what, instead of grounding you, blah, blah, blah, I want you to write a one page story about how you thought you could talk your way out of being grounded."

I'm serious, give it a shot. You might be surprised at what you discover. Your kid might be, too.

No. 3 Reason for Lying: Low Self-esteem

Another reason for ADHD kids telling lies stems from their need to impress you, a misguided attempt at compensating for their low self-esteem. They suspect you think of them as losers, so perhaps if they dress things up a little, you'll become more accepting of who they are or maybe you'll give them some of the attention they crave so badly.

One such kid, Rolf, came to see me with his mother. He'd told her all about his drug habit, his use of cocaine, heroin, and methamphetamines. He claimed he shot up regularly but had now decided to get his act together. So last week he went cold turkey, and boy, she should be so impressed at his courage!

Trouble was, the kid had no track marks on his arms, and had no clue about the procedure for using IV drugs. As far as I could tell, the only drugs he'd ever "used" were aspirin!

Rolf's goal was to get mom's attention (which he sure had now) and convince her that he'd finally done something worthwhile. Being an ADHD kid with an Honesty Disability, most of the messages he'd ever heard from her had been negative. This was the first time she'd ever said how proud she was of him, what with him conquering his drug habit and all!

This mind-set can become a serious problem, because the lower the self-esteem, the greater their attempts at impressing you, so much so, they can lose sight of who they really are, trapped in a web of half-truths, outright lies, and outrageous claims of heroism.

Another kid I know has saved at least forty-eight drowning people from the nearby Meramec River! In the last three months! His ADHD HIT brother has single-handedly beaten up over 1,230 bad guys in the supermarket parking lot who were bothering women shoppers.

A fourteen-year-old often speaks about his father who is a government spy. Suspicious that I was hearing a teensy-weensy fib, I asked him for more details. His reply?

"If I tell you, he might have to kill you."

Enough said.

If these lies and pretenses continue unabated, they'll become so out of control that that kid will have no other choice but to run for Congress or work in Hollywood.

No. 4 Reason for Lying: Boredom

A much simpler explanation for lying is boredom. Having a strong need for excitement and high stimulation, some ADHD kids just make stuff up to watch your reactions and be entertained by them. For these guys, lying and story telling become the preferred method of alleviating boredom.

Again, one possible solution is to channel them into creative writing or screenplay writing. Let's face it, aren't movies just spectacular lies that we pay to see?

The next step is for you to stop reacting to the wild claims and pronouncements. Of course, as part of their experimentation with the world, many teenagers make off-the-wall comments to see how you'll react.

I have to be honest, our seventeen-year-old went through a phase of this recently, and I fell right into the trap every time, overreacting and freaking out in general. I finally figured out what was going on when he made the comment, "Who needs HBO when I've got you!"

In the past week alone at the office, I heard one kid say to his very religious mother, "There is no God. I'm an atheist."

Another told his family he was thinking about becoming a devil worshiper.

A third kid said he was quitting school to become an asphalt man.

But the highlight for this week came from fifteen-year-old Byron who said, "I want a sex change for my sixteenth birthday." Yet being gay or experiencing sexual identity problems were not issues for Byron. He was bored and simply needed some entertainment and attention, both of which he received in great measure.

So if you hear these kinds of set-up statements from your kid, step back and ask yourself what's really behind them— true dilemmas or entertainment?

Incidentally, the quote I used at the start of this section from Sir Walter Scott was amended by another writer, J.R. Pope, in *A Word of Encouragement*, "But when we've practised quite a while, how vastly we improve our style."

Wonder if Mr. Pope had ADHD?

Unofficial Symptom #4: Literal Minimalism

Literal Minimalism means, "If you don't spell it out, you don't mean it, so I ain't doin' it."

One day, a dad needed to run a few errands, and so he asked his ADHD teenage son to mow the lawn. When Dad returned, the front lawn had been mown and Junior stood in the driveway, looking very proud of his accomplishment, grass clippings plastered on his cheerful, sweat-stained face.

Initially, Dad was pleased, too, but when he walked around the side of the house, he noticed the side and back lawns still looked like a jungle.

"Hey, I thought I asked you to mow the lawn," Dad said.

"I did!"

"What about the sides and the back?"

"Huh? You mean the *whole* lawn?" Junior shook his head. "Uh-uh, you didn't say that!"

To an ADHD kid, "Empty the dishwasher," means take the dishes out of the dishwasher and place them on the counter; you didn't say to put them in the cabinets. You didn't say to put the dirty ones in the dishwasher. Or wipe down the counter tops. Or wring out the washcloth. Or turn the dishwasher on again. All you said was empty the dishwasher, which he did, so why are you complaining?

"Clean your room," doesn't necessarily mean make your bed, vacuum, dust, and bring out eighty piles of dirty laundry, most of which has been stuffed under the bed for the last four weeks. Clean your room really means hide all visible objects from sight, either by cramming them into closets or squeezing them into already overflowing drawers.

"Pick your towels up off the bathroom floor," doesn't mean you have to actually hang them on the rail—it means pick them up and dump them in another location, preferably in your sister's room.

Sound familiar? Part ADHD, part teenager laziness, and part airheadedness.

Don't be afraid to spell out the details, and for goodness sakes, don't *ever* dare to presume that he'll figure any of this out by himself.

Unofficial Symptom #5: Obsessive Thinking

Back to computerland. There's not an ADHD kid I know who can't sit still in front of a Nintendo 64/Saturn/Sega/Sony PlayStation for hours on end, and hyperfocus his little brain to mush. Remember, hyperfocus is one of the paradoxes that goes with the condition, the ability to suddenly focus on something to the point of obsession, frequently with a visually stimulating component. This obsessiveness can be so intense that your kid may become a "visual addict," increasing his "dose," and experiencing withdrawal, anger, and irritability when he doesn't have access to his "drug" of choice.

When an ADHD kid goes into the hyperfocus zone, there is almost a Ritalin-like effect—the psychomotor agitation decreases, he feels calm, he's focused, and has a feeling of competence and/or accomplishment.

When a child has many moments each day of feeling incompetent or unsuccessful, *any* activity that provides a sense of mastery can quickly become an addictive behavior.

These areas of competency and mastery are not limited to video games. All sorts of hobbies and other interests can fall into this category. (Note: According to most authorities, passing gas is not a hobby, no matter what your kid tells you.) Lots of people have hobbies and passions, but the ADHD child, adolescent, and even adult, can take them and stretch them to the *nth* degree.

The danger lies in becoming a Jack-of-all trades and master of none, to use a well-worn cliché. One solution is to teach your child new ways of approaching old interests because novelty is an effective way to harness attention and focus.

I once saw a young man who was obsessed with *Star Wars*. From a therapeutic perspective, that was fine as I could get through to him using metaphors and analogies from the movies, all of which made sense to him. He saw me as Yoda, mainly because I'm short and talk funny (my Scottish accent). His seventh grade teacher was Jabba the Hutt.

Problems arose whenever we didn't talk about *Star Wars*. He'd say he was bored, and would stare out the window until we talked *Star Wars* again. This also created social problems as other kids avoided him and poked fun because *Star Wars* was the only subject he would ever talk about!

I used the concept of the "Force" to make some other points, that the "Force" existed in and of itself, but if used obsessively, would turn him into Darth Vader. On the other hand, if used wisely, the "Force" would transform him into Luke Skywalker.

The only problem was when he said, "What's wrong with being Darth Vader? I think he's cool!"

Now we had another therapeutic issue to tackle!

But eventually, we began to make progress because:

a) he realized he had become "boring" to the other kids, one of the things he feared most

b) his parents started putting limits on how much time he spent playing *Dark Forces* and *Tie Fighter*, both *Star Wars* computer games. By gradually reducing his time with the games, Mom and Dad were then able to use time-limited access to the games as a reward for appropriate behavior.

As a result, we were able to create some balance in his life, and now he's a happier, less obsessed child who can talk about subjects other than *Star Wars.*

Unofficial Symptom #6: Fidgeting

Okay, I know fidgeting is an "official" symptom, but I've included it here because fidgeting is so often misunderstood. There's a strong belief that if an ADHD kid is fidgeting or playing with something, then he's not listening or paying attention, yet another paradox. My experience as a teacher and a counselor has been that many ADHD'ers *are* listening when they're fidgeting.

Due to the psychomotor agitation, they can't really focus too well or pay attention unless they have something in their hands with which to anchor themselves. Yet so many times when they're doing this, they're told to stop, even though fidgeting might be the very way in which they *can* pay attention!

When I see a kid zoning out or becoming agitated during a family counseling session, I usually hand him a large paper clip or a small pebble I keep lying around the office for this very reason, much to the surprise of Mom and Dad who'd warned him earlier about not fidgeting during the session.

In my own case, I typically keep a pen handy, kind of like Bob Dole, heir-apparent to the pineapple fortune. Most parents don't really notice, but the kids usually do, and naturally comment, immediately sensing a kindred spirit. I make no excuses; what works, works.

By now, you probably have a basic understanding of the main signs and symptoms of ADHD, official and unofficial. But it's still not that simple. Before we go any further, we need to examine some other conditions that resemble ADHD, the *ADHD Wannabes*.

Chapter 3

ADHD Wannabes

ADHD Wannabes are conditions which on the surface look like true ADHD, but an in-depth assessment and evaluation often reveals they're actually something quite different.

Trauma

A child who lives in a chaotic, verbally/physically/ sexually abusive environment usually has difficulty sustaining attention, may be highly distractible, and spends most of his or her time zoning out as a way to escape the painful reality of his or her life. Given this environment, these behaviors are more often than not symptoms of anxiety and trauma, not necessarily ADHD, (although they can be all three).

Alternatively, a child from a similar environment may be hyperactive, out of control, shoot his mouth off, and be destructive as a way of acting out his distress. Living in a harsh or combative environment doesn't exactly lend itself to strong powers of concentration.

A component of an ADHD evaluation is to rule out the effects of trauma or other conditions with ADHD-like symptoms. If a kid suffering from trauma is mistakenly diagnosed as ADHD, the trauma is largely left untreated, and no amount of ADHD counseling or medication interventions will improve the true situation. In some cases, it may even exacerbate the symptoms.

On the other hand, if a non-ADHD kid suffering from a disorder like Post Traumatic Stress Disorder (PTSD) is taken to a competent clinician for an ADHD evaluation, the clinician should be able to differentiate between the two conditions. Then the *real* problem, namely PTSD masquerading as ADHD, can be addressed. In this case, the ADHD-like symptoms were a means to an end; they brought the child to the attention of a clinician who can now make the appropriate interventions.

Anxiety

Most of us, kids as well as adults have experienced periods of anxiety. You worry, you can't sleep, you're irritable, keyed-up, on edge, and feel down some of the time. But things change, the anxiety passes, and you get on with your life.

However, there is a more long-lasting form of anxiety called Generalized Anxiety Disorder, which looks similar to ADHD. The main symptoms, taken from DSM-IV, are "excessive anxiety and worry for more days than not for at least six months and the child has difficulty controlling the worry, causing significant distress or impairment."

There are six primary symptoms. In adults, three or more are needed to make a diagnosis, but for children, only one is required. I've added the ADHD parenthesis to show the overlap:

1. restlessness or feeling keyed-up or on edge *(ADHD)*
2. easily fatigued
3. difficulty concentrating or mind going blank *(ADHD)*
4. irritability *(ADHD)*
5. muscle tension
6. sleep disturbance (difficulty falling or staying asleep or restless unsatisfying sleep *(ADHD)*

See how close numbers one, three, and four resemble ADHD symptoms. While six is not an official ADHD symptom, sleep problems are common for people with ADHD.

For example, if your kid is being bullied in school, he may appear to develop ADHD PIT symptoms like spacing out and have difficulty concentrating, but these may very well be symptoms of anxiety. If you take him to a clinician who doesn't do a thorough enough assessment, the conclusion might be ADHD. The doctor then puts your already-nervous kid on Ritalin, and now he becomes more revved up and goes through the roof, acts jittery, irritable, and develops sleep disturbances. Instead of helping him, we've made him worse!

The point here is to make sure the clinician really knows the difference between ADHD and the ADHD Wannabes, especially if he or she is prescribing medication.

Dysthymia

A condition in the Depression family of mood disorders, *Dysthymia* is like a low-grade fever—you can go about your business, but you're just not quite functioning at 100 percent. For Dysthymia, the DSM-IV uses the following diagnostic criteria:

A. Depressed mood for most of the day, for more days than not, as indicated either by subjective account or observation by others, for at least two years. *Note*: in children and adolescents, mood can be irritable and duration must be at least one year.

B. Presence, while depressed, of two (or more) of the following:

   (1) poor appetite or overeating
   (2) insomnia or hypersomnia *(ADHD)*
   (3) low energy or fatigue
   (4) low self-esteem   *(ADHD)*
   (5) poor concentration   *(ADHD)*
   (6) feelings of hopelessness

During the two-year period (one year for children or adolescents) of the disturbance, the person has never been without the symptoms in Criteria A and B for more than two months at a time.

Notice three of these symptoms are similar to ADHD, yet you only need two for the clinician to make a diagnosis of dysthymia.

There are other diagnostic criteria with dysthymia but I only wanted to highlight the main ones.

And please, even though you may now have a rudimentary understanding of dysthymia (or the other Wannabes), do not use this book to make a diagnosis. If you suspect your kid is suffering from dysthymia, anxiety, PTSD or ADHD, take him to a licensed clinician for an evaluation.

Central Auditory Processing Disorder: CAPD

Current research suggests there is a strong correlation between ADHD and a condition known as Central Auditory Processing Disorder (CAPD). Basically, a kid with CAPD hears what's being said, but has problems understanding the meaning, storing the information, and responding to it.

CAPD can resemble ADHD because the kid appears not to be listening, isn't paying attention, and/or gives inappropriate responses.

In 1992, the American Speech-Language-Hearing Association defined CAPD as *"limitation in the ongoing transmission, analysis, organization, transformation, elaboration, storage, retrieval, and use of information contained in audible signals."* Quite a mouthful, huh?

This means that although your kid's hearing isn't impaired per se, what he *does* with what he's heard may be. One recent study cited by Ned Hallowell, author of *Driven to Distraction*, estimated that as many as 50 percent of children with CAPD also have ADHD.

ADHD diagnosing is typically done by guys like me in the psychological field or by medical guys like pediatricians, neurologists, and psychiatrists, whereas CAPD is the arena of audiologists and speech/language specialists, highlighting the need for all those disciplines to collaborate with each other. A number of test batteries used in learning disability testing may also pick up CAPD.

CAPD is like being in a foreign country and you don't speak the language, a source of great frustration to many

Americans, I might add, the way those damned foreigners refuse to speak English!

For example, let's take a trip to China. So there you are, standing outside the Great Hall of the People in Beijing taking photographs of military equipment that happens to be rolling by in front of you.

A Chinese military official approaches and you suspect he wants to give you some information about the missiles you're photographing. Understanding him shouldn't be too difficult, because you read a book on the flight over, *How to Talk Chinese for Idiot Tourists.*

He tells you that you're not permitted to photograph military objects of mass destruction. However, given that you're not too swift in his language, what you *really* hear is, "The cheese is old and stinky." At least, that's what you *think* he said, not realizing that he told you not to take photographs or you'll be arrested.

Not wanting to appear ignorant, you smile politely, nod your thanks, and go on taking pictures. Until you're arrested by the People's Department of Idiot Tourists Taking Forbidden Pictures.

To that soldier, you have CAPD. He presumed you understood him because you *pretended* that you did understand. Except you didn't, and now your butt's in a Beijing jail. Sure, go ahead, plead your innocence, but it won't do you any good.

Meanwhile, the soldier says to his comrades, "What's the matter with that guy? I told him clear as day not to take any photographs."

This is what CAPD is like. You hear words, but they don't mean what you *think* they mean.

The condition is subtle, almost invisible, yet can wreak havoc if not identified and treated.

Learning Disabilities

I've included learning disabilities as an ADHD Wannabe due to the considerable overlap between the two conditions, and the fact that a significant number of kids suffer from both ADHD and LD (Learning Disabilities), another reason for making sure your child has a thorough evaluation.

However, they're not the same condition. Dr. Sam Goldstein, a prominent researcher and expert in the field, summarizes LD as a problem of *input* in that the kid can't quite take in or understand the material presented to him, whereas with the ADHD kid, the problem is one of *output* because the kid *does* understand but isn't interested in the material or doesn't feel like applying himself. From an external point of view, both conditions appear to be the same, but as you can see, they're not.

The main signs and symptoms of LD include:

- Difficulty staying on task
- Difficulty remembering
- Poor organization
- Social difficulties
- Difficulty with sequencing
- Difficulty discriminating among sounds
- Poor attention and concentration
- Daydreaming
- Distractibility

As if differentiating between the two conditions wasn't difficult enough, we additionally have to deal with the fact that there are *still* debates over how to define exactly what a learning disability is. Last I heard, there were eleven definitions being touted, with twelve additional sub-definitions!

So, to keep things simpler, I'm using the definition spelled out in Public Law 94-142, the Education for All Handicapped Children Act:

"A disorder in one or more basic psychological processes involved in understanding or in using language, spoken or written, which may manifest itself in an imperfect ability to listen, speak, read, write, spell or do mathematical calculations."

Some kids have very specific learning disabilities, while others have a cluster, ranging from *mild, moderate,* to *severe.*

There's not enough room to do justice to the whole area of LD in this book, so I'll refer you to Sally Smith's *Succeeding Against the Odds*, and Bruce Pennnington's *Diagnosing Learning Disorders*, two books which I recommend to the parents of LD kids.

Specific learning disabilities include the following:

- **Central Auditory Processing Disorder**
- **Dyslexia:** difficulty with reading and writing
- **Dyscalculia:** difficulty with math, algebra
- **Dysgraphia:** difficulty with writing
- **Dyssemia:** difficulty with verbal and non-verbal social cues (discussed in a later chapter)

- **Dysnomia:** difficulty remembering familiar words
- **Dyspraxia:** difficulty making appropriate body responses, motor coordination.
- **Visual Perception Problem:** difficulty in comprehending and interpreting what you see

Just as there is debate over definition, there is also statistical inconsistency between the ADHD and LD figures. For example, kids with *dyslexia*, a learning disability with regard to reading and writing, have a higher incidence of ADHD, although kids with ADHD don't have a higher incidence of dyslexia. However, the statistics keep changing.

I'd like to be able to quote specific correlations and incidences between ADHD and LD but the statistics are so varied they're almost meaningless. Some numbers go from 10 percent all the way up to 80 percent!

For further information on learning disabilities, contact the *Learning Disabilities Association of America* (LDA), 4156 Library Road, Pittsburgh, PA 15234, (412) 341 1515. Each state has its own chapter of the national organization.

Or maybe your kid doesn't have LD but instead, one of the following other conditions:

Following Other Conditions

Sometimes, the reason your child isn't doing so well in school is not because of ADHD, LD, CAPD, NYPD, or any of the other almost-fashionable Ending-in-D-Disorders; the reason he's not doing well is because he's as blind as a bat! (I hate using clichéd metaphors, but it's the only one I could come up with.) No wonder he can't see the chalkboard in class, or take decent notes; he's myopic or maybe even short-sighted, or has one of a dozen other sight related problems. Suggestion: take him to an ophthalmologist and have his eyesight tested.

Or perhaps he has hearing problems and doesn't fully understand auditory instructions. If this is the case, take him to an audiologist.

I know these sound ridiculously obvious but I can't tell you how many kids I've seen whose ADHD cleared up miraculously when they started wearing glasses!

But my all-time favorite ADHD Wannabe is:

Snot-Nosed-Lazy-Brat-Syndrome: (SNLBS)

Over the years, I've seen a number of young men (and even a few young women) who for all the world looked and sounded like they had ADHD, based on the following symptoms:

1. Lack of focus
2. No follow through
3. Refusal to complete assignments
4. Refusal to do homework
5. Tantrums on hearing the word "no"
6. Doesn't listen
7. Doesn't comply with family rules
8. Can be a real pain

An in-depth assessment and evaluation revealed they didn't have ADHD, but were really suffering from a condition known as SNLBS, Snot-Nosed-Lazy-Brat-Syndrome. (Please note: SNLBS is not an official psychological term; I made it up.)

Okay, so how do you tell if your (nah, let's make that someone else's) kid has SNLBS or ADHD?

1. If your child meets the diagnostic criteria for ADHD, and you've ruled out other conditions like anxiety and dysthymia, then you're probably dealing with ADHD.

2. If your (someone else's) child has the above symptoms but *doesn't* meet the ADHD diagnostic criteria, and you've ruled out the other conditions, then you probably *are* dealing with SNLBS.

As with the other ADHD Wannabes, there is some overlap between the symptoms. Any of the ADHD varieties can be mistaken for SNLBS.

In my own case, I appeared to have SNLBS, but in later life I discovered I was really dealing with ADHD CT (Combined Type).

As an ADHD CT child, the inattentiveness was predominant, and in grade school, I spent most of my time standing in the corner for Not Paying Attention or for Talking to My Neighbor. There were two hundred and thirty seven beige-colored bricks on the wall in front of me. I know for a fact because I counted them every day when I was in my corner.

In Glasgow, Scotland, 1969, there was no such thing as ADHD; there were only "Underachievers." I was an "Underachiever," a "No-user," (a person of no use) and my all-time favorite, "A Producer of Unadulterated Rubbish!"

Needless to say, by the time I reached high school, the pattern was ingrained, as you can see from these approximated report card excerpts:

"Doesn't pay attention."
"Insists on talking to his neighbor."
"Doesn't listen."
"Can't tell that boy anything."
"Lives in La La Land."
"Always drawing wee people on his notebook."
"Overactive imagination."
"Makes paper airplanes all the time."
"This has been another good year for Thomas." (Figure *that* one out!)

The pattern continued, and to make matters worse, by the time I was in high school, the hyperactivity was becoming more pronounced as my frustration increased.

In my Junior year at St. Richard the Bonehead's Boarding School For Fine Young Men, my English teacher issued me with a gag order due to my lack of "cooperation."

His main problem with me was that although I read voraciously, I wouldn't read the books he prescribed. I wanted to talk about *Catch-22* and how I related to the character of Yossarian. I also wanted to discuss characterization and dialogue in Ed McBain's *87th Precinct* novels. Snorting his disgust, my teacher said they were "American drivel," and were not on the list of approved literature. *Oliver Twist* and *David Copperfield* were.

"I thought you said no American drivel?"

He peered over the tops of his bifocals. "Excuse me?"

"Well isn't David Copperfield an American magician?" I continued. Anyway, I'd already seen Oliver Twist, the movie.

He ignored me (he was good at that), but I was undeterred. "Okay, how about *A Connecticut Yankee in King Arthur's Court* by Mark Twain? *The Blackboard Jungle*? Honestly, it's by Evan Hunter, not Ed McBain," I bargained.

His only response was that I was nothing but an annoyance, and ordered me not to speak any more as I had nothing of value to contribute to the class.

Deciding I had no other choice but to live up to my annoyance role, I bugged the living daylights out of the guy by asking even more irrelevant questions or making observations like, "Hey, do you know the German word for cotton is baumwolle? Says so right here on my sweater label."

After a while, I gave up, shut my mouth, and started reading *The Blackboard Jungle* in class while he tried to ignore me, an uneasy truce of silent indifference.

But far more interesting than English was Science. Here's an approximation of a letter my parents received:

Dear Mr. & Mrs. Quinn,

We regret to inform you that your son, Thomas, has been withdrawn from Science class. Please be aware he is the first student we have had to do this with since 1923.

Wow! Finally, a scholastic first! I was thrilled, but for some reason, my parents didn't quite share my enthusiasm.

Eventually, they were able to convince me that the real problem wasn't that I was dumb, but that I refused to follow the school's curriculum; I kept insisting on using my own:

Theirs	*Mine*
Math	Astronomy
French	Egyptology
Latin	Psychology
English	Ed McBain novels
History	Photography
Geography	Art
Religion (Catholic)	Religion (the Moonies)
Music	Punk Rock
Study Hall	Mythology
Standing in corner	Botany
Principal's Office	Starsky & Hutch

I'm not talking about cursory interests, either. I studied constantly in the library, fascinated and deeply interested in each topic. I read everything I could get my hands on relating to each subject and took copious notes.

Reluctantly, I began to realize my grades really *were* based on their curriculum, not mine, so out of a class of 25 students, I was always 24th. My underachieving compadre, Heid the Ball (Glasgow slang for he who is a dork as evidenced by his tendencies to play soccer primarily with his head), was always 25th.

Except for Latin. The reason my Latin grades weren't atrocious was that although I was unable to translate hundreds of lines of *The Iliad*, I made up my own versions which my understanding Latin teacher found entertaining. As a result, he always gave me a passing grade because I was at least showing effort in my revisions of Homer (not the Simpson

variety), ergo, I wasn't blowing off the class. He was one of
the few who actually believed in me.

As did my dad. He sure as hell didn't understand anything about how my demented, artistic mind worked, especially with him being an electrical engineer, but he was the
one who always stood by me. No matter how bad my report
cards were, he'd say, "Did you do your best?"

And I could usually say yes. Kind of. Sort of. You know
what I mean. And he would say, "Well, you can only do your
best." He died in 1995. I miss him and being able to call him
up and say, "Hey, do you know the Latin word for Spam is
Epamibus?" and we'd both laugh our butts off. Didn't understand me, but he sure believed in me.

And that's the point of these vignettes; even if you don't
understand your kid or why he does what he does, at least let
him know you're *trying* to understand, that you believe in
him, because I bet by this point, he doesn't believe in himself
anymore.

My math teacher *didn't* believe in me. We used a track
system—the smart kids were in the "A" track, the rest in the
"B" track.

Sophomore year, 1976, staring blankly at a blackboard
filled with the terrifying sight of numbers, sines, cosines, and
other meaningless figures. And my math teacher, staring
down at the obvious look of panic on my face saying, "Quinn,
do you know why you're in the "B" math class?"

I swallowed. Here we go again. I didn't know exactly
what was coming next, but I'd learned from experience that
I'd end up feeling dumb. (For you parents with ADHD
sophomores, can you see why they get to the point where
they don't care any more and seem to give up? They don't

tell you most of the humiliations they experience because they're too embarrassed.)

"Well, Quinn, do you?"

"Do I what?"

"Do you know why you're in the "B" class?"

Already, I could feel my face burning shamefully as the other students turned to face me, grateful they'd been spared.

"No, Father." (The teachers were all priests.)

He grinned. "Because we don't have a *"C"* math class, ha ha."

I was now supposed to be motivated and pay more attention? But I took comfort in knowing that he couldn't draw. See, that was the only single area in which I had any competence, drawing. I was pretty good and drew cartoons of all my teachers on my notebooks, on the desks, on the walls, and I took great delight in knowing that Father Albert Einstein here couldn't. Being able to draw gave me a sense of competency in something. I knew I was a math moron, I felt unsuccessful in other subjects, but at least here was an area that proved to be my salvation in that it stopped me from having a complete nervous breakdown!

When dealing with a kid who has a similar academic history, don't spend *all* your time focusing on what he's *not* good at but give some attention to the areas where he *does* show interest and competency.

Just because he has a difficult time with certain subjects or school in general doesn't necessarily mean he suffers from SNLBS!

In my own case, some of the frustration may have been alleviated through proper assessment, diagnosis, and treatment. Instead of just being an SNLB who was dumb at math, it turns out I had ADHD CT, with a little *dyscalculia* (math learning disability) thrown in for good measure.

On the other hand, if I had received the appropriate intervention, I may never have learned the German word for cotton, information, I might add, that I've used far more often than algebra!

So does he have ADHD, LD, SNLB, or is he just plain dumb?

To find out, turn to the next chapter, *Accurate Diagnosis.*

Chapter 4

So Does He or Doesn't He?
Accurate Diagnosis

When I was an alcoholism and drug abuse counselor, we often used the following adage with our alcoholic patients: "If it walks like a duck, talks like a duck, sounds like a duck, then it's a duck." The same principle applies here. In ADHD terms, if we think we're dealing with a duck we have to make sure we really are, and if so, what kind.

As technology advances, so do our methods for making a diagnosis (from the Greek *"diagn"* meaning "That's" and *"osis"* meaning "what's wrong with you"). Everyone is looking for the definitive "ADHD Test," but we don't have one as such, at least, not yet. Currently, there are two computer tests which help tremendously, the Test of Variable Ability (TOVA), and the Intermediate Visual and Auditory (IVA), developed by Joseph A. Sandford, Ph.D., of Virginia. Of the two tests, I prefer using the IVA because it assesses both visual and auditory attention responses.

Both tests are Continuous Performance Tests (CPT), which means the test will measure the performance of the test-taker over a defined time period.

These tests can assist in reducing clinician and parental bias for or against an ADHD diagnosis, *but* the most important diagnostic tool is still the good old-fashioned personal history.

Not taking a thorough history is like going to a medical doctor with the following complaint:

You: "Hey, doc. I've got a fever."
Doc: (Touches your forehead with the back of his hand) "Yup, feels kinda hot and clammy."
You: "So what's wrong?"
Doc: "Mmm. . . Well, I think there's a fever with Bubonic Plague
You: "Plague? I saw a show about that on "Oprah!" I'll be damned, I've got the plague."
Doc: "Yup, you sure do. Here, take these pills and call me in the morning."

And you go on your merry way, ringing a little hand bell in front of you shouting "Unclean! Unclean!" the way Medieval Europeans did during the Black Death. Even though you're now a social outcast, you feel better because the doctor made a diagnosis.

Anyway, you get the idea. No medical or psycho/social history. No questions about travel to exotic locations, time travel to Medieval Britain, no exams, no tests, cultures, or other assessments, but hey, you thought it might be Bubonic Plague, and so did the doc, and voilá, you've got the plague!

If this is how your clinician conducts assessments and evaluations, it's time you went to someone else.

When taking your child for an evaluation, what should you expect?

1. First of all, a halfway decent assessment should take more than one visit. Even the most severe ADHD kid can fake it, especially with the one-on-one attention of the clinician and the novelty of the situation.

2. Personal/family history: What was he like as a child? Sleeping patterns? Discipline problems? Siblings, any other family members with ADHD? Any alcoholism, depression, or other conditions in the family? Family nicknames can provide clues—mine were "Motor Mouth," "Fidget," "Him-Living-in-Cloud-Cuckoo-Land," and the old favorite, "Ants-in-his-Pants."

3. Medical history: Childhood diseases, head traumas, seizures, infections? Hearing or vision problems? Frequent allergies or ear infections?

4. Educational history: Grades? Poor test-taker or exceptionally good at them? Verbal ability? Reading comprehension? Writing ability? Math skills? Listening skills? Distractible, can't sit still in class, daydreams? Doesn't do homework or hides assignments? Class clown? Zones out, quietly failing subjects, or shows other negative scholastic patterns?

5. Social history: How do other kids relate to him? Does he have a best friend? No friends? Overly shy, avoids other kids? Dominant or submissive? Immature for his age? Ostracized? Avoids conflict or thrives on it? Athletic ability or a total klutz?

6. Psychological history: Is he depressed, talks about being sad/angry/worried much of the time or appears to be and won't talk about it? Tantrums? How's his self-esteem? What's he good at? Are there any areas where he shows competence and talent or does he feel like a schmuck most of the time? Is he overweight and called names? How does he express feelings? Does he spend too much time alone in his room in front of a computer or video game? Does he obsessively spend every waking minute with friends, them being the only thing he lives for? Does he show evidence of a Conduct Disorder or Oppositional Defiance Disorder (don't you love all these labels for obnoxiousness?)

7. Rating Scales: For example, the *Conners Scales* or the *Attention Deficit Disorders Evaluation Scale* by Stephen B. McCarney, which rate observable behavior, in which you check off the behavior patterns you usually see. There are also similar scales for teachers to rate the child in classroom settings.

8. CPT Tests: Continuous Performance Tests like the IVA and the TOVA are controversial in some circles, but I find them useful adjunct tools in making a thorough assessment.

When conducting evaluations, I usually meet with Mom and Dad first (if I'm dealing with a two-parent family), and then I spend time with their child. Later, I give Mom, Dad, and their child my *initial impressions* because it's still too early to make a definitive diagnosis.

At the second session, I continue the fact-finding mission, using check scales and narratives. I like written narratives, especially from educators, for two main reasons:

    a) a narrative means the educator has probably put some thought into what he or she is saying

    b) if we're dealing with a kid who doesn't quite fit into the checklist formula, a narrative helps fill in the missing blanks

If I receive a report like the following, I've been given specific information in a way I might not receive via checklists:

Dear ADHD Counseling Guy:

Bart is the class clown, but sometimes he just sits and looks out the window oblivious to what's going on around him. He fires spit balls almost daily despite facing the consequences. He answers back. He asks me to defend my position as an authority figure. He has a tendency to focus on bodily functions such as passing gas and belching loudly. Yet when he chooses, he can write the most profound poetry with obvious talent and emotion. However, if I try to read his work aloud to the class, he pitches a fit.

He has not turned in his last thirty-six assignments even though I know for a fact he has completed thirty-four of them.

If he has a burning question in his mind like who the St. Louis Cardinals are playing this week, even though we're in the middle of a test, he'll get up out of his seat, walk to the other side of the class, and ask another student. He then appears surprised that I'm angry.

Yet, when he sits in front of a computer monitor, he becomes so focused, I can't get him away from the screen.

Sincerely,

Miss Cynthia T. Thunderflash

This tells me a lot about Bart. If I have several of these from other teachers; info from Mom and Dad, brothers and sisters, and even the kid himself; have ruled out the ADHD Wannabes; have seen a positive score on the IVA test; and the kid meets the diagnostic criteria in the DSM-IV psychiatric manual, I'm now in a much stronger position to make an accurate diagnosis.

But sometimes despite all this evidence, a skeptical parent or teacher might say, "So, he's ADHD, big deal. We've known that for years."

And I would say, sure you have but now that you have an official name for his behavior, you can exert more appropriate management and treat the problem accordingly.

And reluctantly they say, "Okay, so let's load him up with Ritalin and he'll be fine. I saw that on "The Jerry Springer Show."

Uh-uh, it's not that simple. While some medications— Ritalin, Adderall, Cylert and Dexedrine—can be highly effective, just popping a couple of those babies every day ain't quite gonna cut it.

You, as a family, as well as your child, need to learn a new set of skills for managing ADHD, because years of untreated ADHD may have created unhealthy family dynamics and power struggles which won't be alleviated solely by medication.

Again, I stress the importance of seeing a counselor with solid experience and a working knowledge of ADHD. If the counselor attended a workshop in 1989 on *Behavioral Management of ADD Children* but hasn't read a thing since nor consulted with knowledgeable colleagues, you might want to meet with a counselor who has a tad bit more experience.

Remember the beginning of this chapter, if it walks like a duck, looks like a duck, etc.? This also applies to counselors, psychologists, pediatricians, psychiatrists—if it looks like a quack (see, there's that duck again), walks like a quack, talks like a quack, then run! You don't want you or your kid dealing with a quack!

The good news is that if a diagnosis of ADHD *is* made, then it really is good news because that means there are now a whole bunch of things he *isn't*—a drug addict, criminally insane, psychotic, stupid, or lazy. A proper diagnosis tells us there's a reason why he forgets so much or seems to live on another planet, that his purpose on Earth isn't just to ruin your life. And while ADHD isn't curable as such, it's certainly highly treatable with counseling, family counseling and appropriate medication.

The bad news is that initially, some parents do see a diagnosis as bad news, especially in cases where the dad has undiagnosed ADHD himself. Parents can become upset, even angry, that they have to face the fact that their once-perfect child is officially imperfect.

For example:

> *Me:* "Johnny has ADHD, Hyperactive-Impulsive Type."
>
> *Dad:* "Ain't nothing wrong with that boy a good kick in the pants won't fix." (said while staring around the room)
>
> *Me:* "I thought you said you'd already tried that."
>
> *Dad:* "Yeah, but I guess I ain't been doing it hard enough," (said tapping his feet and drumming his fingers).
>
> *Me:* "Well, according to what your wife here has told me, what Bart himself has told me, what the teachers have reported, the observations I've made and the IVA test, it really does look as if he has ADHD."
>
> *Dad:* (leaping out of seat and walking around in circles, playing with a crystal paper weight he removed from my desk) "Listen, that boy's just like me, that's all. No difference between us. A chip off the old block."
>
> (Wife glances at me, rolls her eyes as if to say, "See? I've got two of them on my hands!")
>
> *Dad:* "Oh, and by the way, you see that Rams game the other night? Man, that was a fiasco. Anyway, you were saying something about my kid . . ."

There's no point in me trying to argue; that would be a lose-lose proposition for both of us. As an ADHD counselor, my best option is the same best option as the family's—education, patience, and persistence.

Instead of meeting with Bart at the next session, I'll talk with Dad alone, and try to answer his many questions, leading him toward the facts of ADHD. Who knows, by the time we're finished, I may soon be evaluating *him*. Not the first time that's happened, and it certainly won't be the last, especially when there's such a strong correlation between ADHD fathers and ADHD sons. Like alcoholism and depression, this one runs in families, too.

Another reason some parents don't like hearing the diagnosis is because of guilt and shame. Where did we go wrong? What could we have done differently? How come we didn't see this earlier? As a result of these feelings, they may brush off the diagnosis to alleviate their guilt.

The truth is, much of this guilt is unfounded because many parents do go out of their way to help their struggling child. They take him to counseling, hire tutors, enroll him in special needs programs, change pediatricians, and even try various bizarre herbal preparations like "New Improved ADD-Begone!" or "ADHD Antidote Pills."

A more positive parental reaction is that when they discover their child really does have ADHD, they exclaim, "I knew it! All along, I've known something was wrong. I knew he was different but have never been able to put my finger on the exact problem."

Now they have some answers. Even the kids do. As one fifteen-year-old boy said recently, "I told you I wasn't like other kids. They all could study and listen but I spent most of my time looking out the window at clouds seeing if I could make out the shape of a hot babe. I really did want to learn, but as soon as I tried, I'd suddenly feel bored. Then I'd feel bad because I knew I was turning into a total loser. Then I decided if I ignored everything, it would go away, so I'd stare at the clouds again to see if I could find the outline of Pamela Anderson Lee. You're telling me this means I'm not a moron, I'm not a total loser, I'm not a whacko—I'm just an ADD'er? Cool!"

Upon hearing a diagnosis, the most common reaction of all, for both parents and child, is relief. Relief that there are now answers, that there's something we can do to fix the situation, that there's light at the end of this very long tunnel.

Okay, now what? Treatment, that's what, coming up in Chapter 5

Chapter 5

Treatment
How Do We Fix Him?
(Not at the Vet's)

Having concluded that we are, indeed, dealing with ADHD, we can now begin treatment. The first step is to teach bother parents and child how the ADHD brain works.

Education

To put it crudely, the ADHD brain seems to engage in a series of "misfires," one of the first pieces of information I pass along to a family. I then go on to explain that ADHD is a neurological biological condition, not just a poor attitude or laziness.

This was demonstrated in 1990 by Dr. Alan Zametkin and his team at the National Institutes of Mental Health. Zametkin where they studied the brain activity of a group of adults, twenty-five with ADHD, and a control group of fifty without ADHD.

Zametkin wanted to measure how their brains metabolized glucose by using a PET scan (Positron Emission Tomography), a camera which measures radioactively-tagged glucose in the brain.

Comparing the radioactive "Kodak moments" of both groups, Zametkin found that the ADHD group metabolized glucose about 8 percent slower than the control group.

The lowered metabolism was most noticeable in the prefrontal areas of the brain, which regulates behavior, impulsivity and the ability to think ahead. (*Now* do you see why they can be such airheads?) In other words, the slower glucose-burn seemed to be responsible for some of the more common ADHD symptoms. Zametkin might not have been able to say *what* exactly caused it, but he sure was able to show us *how* it worked.

For decades, we knew that if you gave a hyper kid stimulants, he'd calm down, a phenomenon that we call a *paradoxical reaction*. Although we knew the phenomenon existed, we didn't really know what *caused* it. Using the work of Zametkin and others, a number of researchers theorized that when we give an ADHD'er a stimulant like Ritalin, the medication speeds up the metabolic rate of glucose in the frontal areas of the brain, "normalizing" them, thus eliminating or decreasing many of the symptoms.

But just knowing this won't change anything; we have to move on to the next stage, counseling, to learn how to bring about lasting change.

Counseling

Although medication can produce dramatic improvements in some kids, counseling is the cornerstone of any successful ADHD treatment. Over the years, kids and their parents usually develop numerous behavioral and communication habits which aren't exactly the most effective or the most healthy. Counseling teaches them to recognize and eliminate these negative behaviors, attitudes, and family dynamics by teaching new, effective parenting techniques and communication skills.

For ADHD kids to become successful, you may have to act more like a personal manager at first, until he gets the idea. (Yeah, I know, you shouldn't be hand-holding teenagers or have to remind them to perform certain tasks, and I know all the experts and academics talk about not enabling, personal accountability, logical and natural consequences, and all the other parenting "shoulds," but you know what, I bet more than half of them have never lived with an ADHD kid!)

So, you do a little handholding—big deal. Sure beats having another nervous breakdown while trying to convince your ADHD teenager that you should only have to tell him to do something once. This is a great theory, and even a personal dream of mine, but in the real world, things aren't quite that cut and dried. It's true, you *should* only have to tell him once, but it's going to take time to reach that point, most likely in the year 2015.

With regard to advice from all the experts, the bottom line is that everyone has an opinion and a pet theory. So as well as listening to the experts, you need to experiment and find out what works best for you and your kid.

When experimenting, try to keep things simple. Have you ever noticed how easily discussions and confrontations rapidly escalate into confusion? Teenagers as a group are very proficient at this. The more vague they are and the more confused you become, the greater the chances of them getting off the hook. Throw in a little ADHD thinking, and pretty soon you've lost before you've even begun.

In the 80's, a common saying in the Recovery movement was Keep It Simple, Stupid (KISS). The same principle applies when dealing with ADHD kids or teenagers.

Another important point to learn through counseling is how to teach your kid about cause and effect—if you do "A" then you make "B" happen.

But his job is to convince you and himself that there's no such thing as cause and effect in a random Universe.

You: "I thought you said you'd done your homework."

Kid: "I can't find it."

You: "Homework, or you're not going out this weekend."

Kid: *Thinks*: What's she talking about? The weekend doesn't exist—this is only Thursday. How can there be consequences at the weekend if there's no such thing as the weekend? "Whatever."

You: "Well? I'm waiting."

Kid: Oh, man! "The dog ate my homework. No, wait! That's not true. I was abducted by aliens, honestly, and I left my assignment notebook on their UFO."

You: "You're grounded for the weekend."

Kid: "I don't care."

You: "You watch your attitude, young man!"

Kid: "Why, does it do tricks?"

You: "Grounded for two weekends."

Kid: "Oh, yeah? Bet you've never seen the inside of an alien mothercraft, huh?"

At which point you feel like screaming. Instead, you head for the fridge and eat four pounds of ice cream (not that cardboard-tasting frozen yogurt garbage) straight out of the carton, then sit down wondering what you did wrong because the 3,758 self-help and parenting books you read all said that

if he does "A," he'll immediately realize he's created consequence "B," and that'll fix everything. *Wrong!*

One of the reasons ADHD kids have a hard time grasping that action "A" equals consequence "B" is because "B" is
in the future. You may not hear too much about this aspect of
ADHD, but there's a time perception problem inherent to the
condition. In many ADHD minds, there is no past (which is
why you don't see much remorse when he does something
wrong—the incident is now in the past, which no longer exists). There's certainly no future, so what's all this nonsensi-
cal garbage about future consequences?

Nope, in the World of the Great Impulsive, only one time
exists—the eternal here and *now!* Which also means that
when there are problems or difficulties, you have to deal with
them *now* or pretty soon you'll be arguing whether or not
they really happened in the first place.

When he refuses to comply with a request, you deal with
the situation immediately, not four hours from now. You
hammer home the point that action "A" equals consequence
"B." Again and again. Over and over.

Okay, so what are all these consequences? Grounding
him? Not exactly the most creative parenting technique, and
certainly not the most effective. Traditional parenting approaches don't always work too well with these kinds of kids.

Let's face it, when your kid acts like a jerk or defies you,
your initial response is probably anger. He knows this, which
means he also knows how to play you like a cheap violin.
You have to start changing your predictable, traditional responses and loosen up. If you don't, you're falling straight
into the trap.

I know the following parenting techniques may raise a
few eyebrows, but much of the time they work (the tech-

niques, not the eyebrows) often simply because they're so unexpected. By not using the same old ineffective parenting techniques, you start to reclaim some of your parental power and authority.

Creative Parenting Techniques

1. Didn't do his homework? Fine, tell him as many unfunny adult (I don't mean X-rated) jokes that you can come up with, all at the same time.

2. Sing to him. I'm serious! Nothing makes an adolescent cringe more than a parent singing directly to him. They especially hate songs by Barry Manilow, Neil Diamond, and Neil Sedaka. Think this sounds weird? Don't you realize this is a well-established technique used by the ATF, FBI, and other organizations in hostage situations? Learn from the masters. Oh, and that bloody awful song Barney the Dinosaur sings, "I love you, you love me, blah, blah, blah . . ." Many kids *hate* that one more than the others combined!

3. To really up the ante, sing in front of his really cool friends, or at least tell them lousy jokes.

4. Dress like a dork. Our oh-so-fashion-conscious kids beg for mercy if I go put on my multi-colored Hawaiian shorts and orange polyester wide collar shirt from the 70's, then parade around in front of their, like, really cool friends.

5. He wants to go out with his friends but you tell him he has to do his homework. Instead of arguing, agree completely that you realize his friends are, indeed, more important than schoolwork, and how nice it'll be to have his little friends buying burgers and hot-dogs from his hot-dog stand after he graduates from Processed Animal Parts University.

6. Make him watch old re-runs of "Hee-Haw," "The Lawrence Welk Show," or "The Brady Bunch."

7. Use "Reverse Psychology." Kid won't stop cursing? The more you ask him to stop, the more he curses? Fine, order him to curse non-stop for ten minutes each day in front of you. Of course, by this point, he'll become nervous and less cocky because you've obviously gone ahead with that nervous breakdown you always threatened to have. This is a family systems technique known as "prescribing the symptom." Instead of trying to stop a behavior, you make him do it more: "Okay, Billy, I want you to call me a f%$#@##$ *&%$#@#! fifty-three times. Okay, start cursing, *now!*" (I bet you anything he refuses!) But traditional parenting? Forget it. Immediately sets you up for a power struggle, and let's face it, aren't you a little tired of power struggles and emotionally charged drama? Don't get me wrong, I'm not suggesting you make light of all situations or that you shouldn't take them seriously, but I am suggesting you don't need to freak out, because how many times have you flipped your cork and nothing's really changed?

ADHD counseling should also involve learning new methods of structure and organization:

Structure

Structure is one of the most feared words for an ADHD'er, child, adolescent, or adult. The thought of structure sends shivers of terror down ADHD spines, creating a knee-jerk, oppositional response, usually accompanied by phrases like, "You're not the boss of me!"

When most ADHD'ers hear the word "structure," what they really hear is torture. The word also smacks of routine, which in turn, translates as boring, another major fear.

Yet, despite their initial fear, many ADHD'ers flourish and become highly successful when they do operate from within a certain structure.

The trick is to come up with a way of *selling* them the idea of having structure, so that they believe they came up with it by themselves. If they think *they* developed the structure, well, now, that's a whole different story.

On numerous occasions, I've made certain suggestions about structure, presenting them in ways that sound as if the kid came up with them himself. He agrees to them, and excitedly, we tell Mom and Dad. But Dad says, "What? I've attempted that a gazillion times and he blew me off but when you say it one time, he thinks it's cool?"

Afraid so. And then I tell Dad that my own kid would listen to him long before he'd listen to me. That's just the way it goes.

In the initial stages of counseling, I tend to avoid using the word "structure." Instead, I'll talk about "game plan," "program," or "I'll-show-them-plan," whatever words I think will be more acceptable to the kid.

There's no way around the fact that you do need a routine of some sort in order to become successful. However, said routine doesn't have to be boring.

For example, I hate exercise with a passion, but I still need to do it. My routine/structure is to get up at 6:00 A.M. and walk until 6:40 A.M. Sounds incredibly monotonous but not if I throw in some novelty. Mondays, I walk around the subdivision. Tuesdays, I walk around the subdivision, but this time in the opposite direction looking in people's windows. Wednesdays, I go to the local park and take every off-the-beaten-path track I can find, usually stumbling upon white tail deer, raccoons, wild turkeys, and on one bizarre occasion, a middle-aged couple having wild sex in the cab of a pick-up truck! Thursdays, I use a Sony Walkman to listen to an audiotape of a novel. Fridays, I continue listening to the novel, and on Saturdays, I walk to the neighboring subdivision to see if those people have any better taste than my immediate neighbors, one of whom has a serious landscaping disability—purple siding with twenty-seven hot pink plastic flamingos strewn around their postage stamp size yard. I swear! On Sundays, I eat donuts.

This is just one small example of how you can take a seemingly boring activity and spice it up a little, yet some form of structure still remains.

Structure in the Home

I don't care how much parents rant and rave about how unstructured their ADHD kid is—if their home is a disaster area, they won't see much improvement in their kid. Sure, with both parents working, kids' after-school activities, and constant demands on their time, it's hard to keep a routine in a household, but if the parents have *no* routine, how can they expect their ADHD kid to be organized if he's surrounded by chaos?

Any time I've helped parents become more structured themselves with the physical environment (I don't do windows), many have commented on how much progress their ADHD son or daughter is making.

Structure also means going to bed at roughly the same time every night, getting up at the same time in the morning, and doing homework in the same place at the same time. Of course, you need to have some degree of flexibility, but as long as there is some routine and predictability, you should start seeing progress.

There's a later chapter on structuring schoolwork and homework.

Get Organized

Structure goes hand in hand with organization, another seeming impossibility for your average ADHD kid. There's even an ADHD sub-diagnosis called *RDKD (Really Disorganized Kid Disorder)*. Symptoms include:

1. Doesn't file things, *piles* them instead—piles of books, piles of toys, piles of unmatched socks, etc.

2. Hangs articles of clothing, including bathroom towels, on the floor.

3. Small woodland creatures have been known to nest in his book bag.

4. 498 school assignments are due within the next forty minutes, then he yells at you like it's all your fault he can't find them.

5. Gives you permission slips for school outings three days after the class has already been to the zoo.

6. Hands you progress reports for you to sign from two years ago.

7. Owns 367 odd shoes. The matching ones have all vanished, having been scarfed by the homework-eating wildebeest or have been beamed aboard an alien mothercraft.

8. You have a discount card from the key engraving department of Sears, a bonus for being the only customer who has had 2,674 house keys made in the last six months.

9. In severe cases, he doesn't quite remember which school he attends.

10. His bedroom appears to have been attacked by a pack of mad dogs and/or a Viking raiding party, usually within fifteen minutes of it having been cleaned by you. (You thought you could wait him out, didn't you? Ha!)

(I made RDKD up, too, so please don't try to persuade your pediatrician that he or she's falling behind in ADHD research!)

Have you ever noticed that when your child is faced with a number of tasks, he avoids all of them to the point of making up the most ridiculous excuses, and argues with you for six hours rather than spend ten minutes actually completing the tasks?

Believe it or not, ADHD kids and adults don't procrastinate just to annoy you. Okay, maybe a few of them do, but in general, the reason is because when faced with a sequence of tasks, they quickly become overwhelmed and don't know where to begin. In addition, how many times have they started to complete a task but you complained because the way they went about it was illogical or plain weird? After a number of years of this self-doubt, the experience of being overwhelmed worsens.

Jack, a seventeen-year-old explains: "If I do it wrong or can't figure out the best way to start, my parents yell at me. Sometimes they let out this big, loud sigh which makes me feel like a total dork, like I'm the Loser of the World. So then I decide to pretend I don't hear them but they yell at me even more and make me feel like an even bigger dork."

The following tips are simple methods that I've found useful for increasing structure and organization:

Post-It Notes™

Those little sticky squares of yellow reminder paper from the 3M company can be a godsend to ADHD'ers. Stick reminders on bathroom mirrors, dashboards of cars, computer screens, assignment notebooks, wherever there needs to be a reminder. (By the way, if you stick them on your kid's forehead, they fall off—I tried that a few weeks ago.) There's even a computerized version from 3M that pops up on your computer screen.

Electronic Organizers

Many ADHD kids have been told to use appointment books and schedules. The only problem is they don't look at their appointment books, assuming they've even written anything down to begin with! A way around this is to switch to an electronic organizer, such as the CASIO Business Organizer Scheduling System (BOSS). Almost like a mini-computer, the BOSS has a *To Do List, Telephone Directory, Memo, Calculator, Reminder, Scheduler, Calendar,* and *Expense* section. Another advantage to this neat little gizmo is that for the ADHD mind, playing with all the buttons and keys can be highly entertaining. My experience has been that the kids I've recommended them to have actually used them.

(Incidentally, neither the 3M company nor CASIO has paid me to say these nice things about their products. Naturally, if they are so inclined, they can send large cash donations to me via the publisher. And the manufacturer of Ritalin? They owe me an absolute fortune, or at least a free lifetime supply.)

Laptop Computers

These might not be practical for all high school students because of cost, and because some schools don't allow students to use them during class, but for those fortunates who do have access to laptops, they are a tremendous help. Many ADHD kids have terrible handwriting and take extreme measures to avoid writing. By using a laptop, these same kids start taking notes, and can even read back what they've written afterwards! Doing homework on a laptop or desktop computer may also be an option, as long as they don't spend every waking moment in "chat rooms" instead of completing book reports.

Other Tips on Structure

1. Prioritize: If he has five tasks before him, show him how to decide on which one is the most important, either because of time restraints or other demands, followed by the second most important and so on. If you yourself have difficulty with prioritizing, ask your counselor or someone else to teach you.

2. Baby Steps: This was one of my favorite counseling expressions until Bill Murray's movie, *What About Bob,* was released. If you've seen the movie, you'll know why. Becoming overwhelmed happens so easily. Take one task, then break that down into "baby steps," so that he's not overwhelmed into a "freeze" response.

3. Monitor his progress: Don't just say, "Here's a bunch of baby steps, good luck," then walk away, expecting him to continue all by himself until the

task is completed. Help him out best you can until he demonstrates proficiency.

4. Time management: If you expect him to work on one task all the way through for a whole hour, forget it! If there's an hour's worth of homework, break the hour up into thirteen minutes, two-minute break, another thirteen minutes and two-minute break, or some other such combination. Reducing time spans allows time perception to become much more manageable to the ADHD mind.

Treatment Sabotage

The dark side of treatment is called "treatment sabotage," and I say dark side because it's unpleasant to think that parents would engage in this type of behavior, but unfortunately, treatment sabotage is a reality we have to contend with in certain families.

These are the parents for whom their child's ADHD offers them a way to avoid dealing with other problems within the marriage or family. A married couple may have had on-going marital problems for years, but they always had their scapegoating, acting-out kid to focus on, allowing them to duck and dodge the painful problems between them.

Somehow (usually because their kid has screwed up so often) they end up in counseling, and discover their son has ADHD. Amazingly, the kid starts cleaning up his act, takes his medication religiously, improves his grades, and becomes more organized.

But to his astonishment and puzzlement, his parents are now on his case more than ever. Feeling hurt, confused, and betrayed, he's tempted to give up and go back to being the way he was, a prime example of treatment sabotage.

But if he's showing so much progress, why on earth would his parents be on his case? Wouldn't they be happy with his progress?

The answer is no because of a phenomenon known as *changeback reaction*, a dynamic which occurs when members of a dysfunctional family attempt to *change* things *back* to the way they used to be. Back then, even though family life was chaotic and painful, at least it felt familiar. Everyone knew where they stood. Unfortunately, everyone was in denial.

Junior's ADHD trouble-making and acting out served as a convenient smokescreen for their troubled marriage/family life. No longer having their smokescreen, thanks to Junior's success, they're once again faced with having to deal with all the painful realities they've "successfully" avoided for years.

As a result, and many times unwittingly, the parents attempt to sabotage their child's progress, because they need him back in his sacrificial lamb role to maintain the dysfunctional status quo.

For Junior, being a scapegoat feels very familiar, almost comfortable, after years of being in that particular role, so before you know it, he forgets to take his Ritalin, loses his appointment scheduler, and skips counseling sessions. His grades start to drop again, he starts to feel bad about himself, and begins to act out. But the family breathes a sigh of relief that they've returned to their "normal" chaotic existence. The parents no longer have to deal with their marital unhappiness any more, and can once again focus on Junior and his growing rap sheet of screw-ups.

A good counselor will recognize the potential for treatment sabotage before it actually begins, and take steps to prevent it from occurring. (Another reason why I place so much emphasis on involving the whole family in treatment.) The concept of "Here's our loony kid, fix him, but we're all fine," is a treatment sabotage warning sign right from the start.

But perhaps it's not the parents who are the saboteurs, but another family member. Again, the experienced counselor needs to be on the lookout for which family members might have an unconscious investment in undermining the ADHD kid's progress, including brothers and sisters who feel that their limelight has been stolen, now that the "bad" kid is being "good."

A common ploy is to set up the ADHD kid by secretly frustrating him to the point that he'll start losing his temper, and all his old behaviors will kick in. Before you know it, he's back in his scapegoat role.

Preventing treatment sabotage takes commitment and ruthless honesty with yourself. ADHD treatment in general is like any other worthwhile venture; you get out of it what you put into it. The more invested *you* are, the more invested your child is, and vice versa.

Counseling should be regular, without skipping appointments for this lame reason or that lame reason. Having a counseling appointment here and there, whenever a crisis erupts, is like trying to use a Band-Aid for an auto wreck! Effective counseling requires patience. Yet at the same time, treatment shouldn't have to take three sessions a week for the next ten years.

And despite what some unrealistic, quality-reducing managed care companies and insurance companies claim, you cannot effectively treat ADHD in three sessions! I'll argue that one with anyone! Contrary to what the above-mentioned managed care companies will also tell you, good, solid, effective psychotherapy is an *art*, not a mechanistic science because we're dealing with the human mind and heart, not a Pentium II computer!

Of course, each kid and family is unique, but you should start seeing changes within a matter of weeks or months, maybe even a year or so in severe cases, depending on how committed the family is. If you do enter counseling with your kid, you have to show the way, demonstrate commitment, patience, and a willingness to follow through with change.

Having emphasized the importance of family involvement in treatment, we now need to look at the specifics of various family members, beginning with moms, the topic of the following chapter.

Chapter 6

Moms:

Heroines of the ADHD World

As I just mentioned, ADHD not only affects your child, but affects *all* family members one way or another, moms in particular (unless you're an ADHD PIT mom, in which case you probably haven't noticed).

You lie awake worrying how your kid will ever make it in this big, bad world. He's such a dreamer, such a little space cadet, the world will suck him up and spit him back out in tiny pieces.

Your daughter can get lost in aisle seven of the supermarket, and now she's talking about going away to college, five states away . . .

Your teenage, hyperactive-impulsive, Quit-Staring-At-Me-Or-I'll-Kick-Your-Butt son announces he wants to take his driver's test. Your hands shake, and you have heart palpitations at the thought of how he'll react if someone cuts him off on the highway when he's sitting behind the wheel of 3,000 pounds of deadly steel . . .

You've spent most of your life micromanaging (from the Greek, *"microman,"* meaning "The Whole Nine Yards") his impulsive behavior, putting out fires (hopefully not literally) on a daily basis, dashing from crisis to crisis, and negotiating peace treaties between him and his ADHD father who's going to kill him when he finds out about the latest escapade!

How many times have you cringed when you answered the phone only to hear the dreaded sound of the principal's voice on the other end, and you wonder what your kid's done *this* time?

Or what about that time when he was three-years-old and went bonkers in the supermarket, and all those judgmental other moms gave you that condescending look as if to say, "What's her problem? Doesn't she know all that brat needs is a good spanking!"

Or when you took him to the swing park, and all the other kids and moms scattered when they saw you coming because your ADHD kid had a few—how can I put this—let's just say he missed certain social cues, and typically ended up pushing the other kids off the swings, then he'd have a tantrum because the other kids wouldn't play with him, and you hid your tears, and felt angry with him and sorry for him all at the same time, and you wondered what you had done wrong to deserve all this?

No one ever seemed to understand. All you heard were snide remarks and well-meaning advice from friends and professionals, none of whom had a clue about ADHD:

Pediatrician: "Just ignore him."
Teacher: "I can tell him nothing."
Priest/Minister: "We all have our crosses to bear."
Mother-in-law: "You're just a lousy mother, honey."
Neighbor: "Something ain't right with that kid."
Sister-in-law: "Lock him in a closet till he's twenty."
Other kids: "Hide! Here comes Hyper Harry!"
Other moms: "Poor Kathy. Glad my kid's not a psycho!"

None of them realized what you were dealing with, and most of their advice was, indeed, well intentioned, but as you may have heard before, "The road to Hell is paved with good intentions."

You're thirty-nine-years-old, but you feel eighty-nine, and you wonder whatever happened to all your dreams and fantasies of a June Cleaver family life. (That was your first problem—Hollywood lied! June Cleaver didn't exist.)

How many mothers constantly blame themselves for not doing enough? Thousands, tens of thousands, all wondering where they went wrong.

As a mom, you make sacrifices and willingly give up some of who you are, but many of you become so lost in the process, completely possessed and obsessed by the problems brought about by your kid's ADHD. Sometimes you feel as if you're being submerged in quicksand and no one even notices!

By taking on so many roles—psychologist, teacher, detective, policeman, fight-breaker-upper, cook, maid, chauffeur, advocate, lawyer, judge, jury, diplomat—you lose who you are. Remember, if you try to be everything to everyone, you end up being nothing to anyone, least of all yourself.

In order to simplify your life, you need to understand which roles you operate from, then learn how not to keep falling into these roles. Most of them are variations of the following—the Micromanager, the Diplomat, and the Blessed Martyr.

Common Mom Roles

Mom Role #1: The Micromanager

Living with constant anxiety for and about your child, you learn to become the ultimate manager, trying to control every tiny detail of his life. Sure, he needs a ton of help and management, but eventually, you become so consumed by the role, you start resenting him for being such a pain, and he resents you for being such a control freak.

He becomes passive-aggressive or outright hostile, frustrating you further, and you end up being even more of the bad guy, the nag, the complainer, and the control freak. The sad part is, you really have turned into a control freak, panicking any time you feel the "illusion" of control slipping away from your iron-fisted grasp.

This is further exacerbated if your child's father suffers from Ostrich Syndrome, burying his head in the sand, refusing to accept that your child (a.k.a. the next President of the United States or at least the next Michael Jordan) even *has* ADHD! He tells you to quit overreacting, that's just the way boys are. Half the time, he doesn't even notice there's anything wrong!

So what can you do? If you don't do everything, you just *know* nothing will ever get done, and the whole family will fall apart, and you'll feel even more out of control than you do now. That's what Sandy thought, too. Here's her story:

Sandy is a forty-two-year-old, married woman with a sixteen-year-old ADHD boy, Todd. He's a good kid with ADHD PIT, the Inattentive Type. A really good kid. *But* he's always late for school, never puts anything away, loses assignments, forgets to bring assignments to school, keeps failing grades, and creates a low-key, fidgety chaos wherever he goes.

Sandy also has a fourteen-year-old daughter, Patty. Todd refers to her as the "Golden Girl," because she's seemingly perfect—excellent grades, popular, involved in team sports, the All-American Girl. Except she doesn't help around the house too much because she has so many things to do, places to go, boyfriends to dump.

Sandy's husband, Phil, is a good guy. He's a respected engineer with a well-known defense contractor, works all day, and is usually exhausted when he comes home. He also has a tendency to tune Sandy out when she complains about always having too much to do between taking care of the kids and running the household.

I asked her about her situation:

"So, Sandy, you don't work outside the home?"
"No, I work, too. I'm an RN at St.Cecilia's Hosptial."
"Oh, so you have a career just like Phil?"
"Four twelve-hour shifts each week."
"Who does the kids' laundry?"
"Me."
"You make their beds in the morning?"
"I guess I do that, too."
"Cleans house?"
"I do."
"Kids dental appointments, doctors, school conferences, kid sporting events, that sort of thing?"
"I guess I take care of that stuff."
"Cooks?"

"Me." (Her voice sounds weary)

"Dishes?"

"Well, the kids don't really like doing that. When I ask them to help, they argue. It's easier for me just to do them myself."

"Why doesn't Phil help?"

"He's tired, kind of crabby in the evenings."

"Can't he help with the laundry?"

She laughs. "Phil doesn't know how to use the washer and drier. The one and only time he did, he dyed all the clothes pink and shrunk half of them."

Incidentally, Phil designs and tests sophisticated weapons systems for the defense contractor, but yet he can't figure out how to turn a dial that says HOT/COLD, COLD/COLD!

Now it was my turn to laugh. That's the oldest trick in the book for us guys. In fact, as little boys, we're sent to a secret training camp to learn how to act like "helpless dumb males." We learn that if we screw up, you'll decide it's easier and faster to do it yourself.

Around 11:45 P.M., Sandy staggers into the bedroom, exhausted, and tries to read a self-help book, *Why Your Life Stinks!* but she passes out by the second word on the page. Before she realizes, the alarm goes off, and she wakes up feeling as if she's had a good rest of about twenty seconds. Stumbling into the kitchen, she spends the next half-hour arguing with Todd who insists on going to school in the clothes that he slept in. He can't find one of his shoes. He refuses to take the dog for a walk before going to school because his stupid Golden Girl sister never has to walk the dog and it's not fair! The final argument is over the location of his book bag, yet again.

At this point, Phil strides into the kitchen, demanding to know where she put his red "power" tie. Doesn't she know he has an important meeting with a bunch of Chinese arms dealers this morning? Then he stomps off cursing under his breath because he doesn't have a freshly ironed and lightly starched white shirt. His mother always had one waiting for him when he lived at home . . .

You see, Phil also has an Ironing Disability, as well as his Washer and Drier Disability.

Todd suggests that red ties are only for dorks, then runs out the front door to catch the school bus, which is disappearing down the street . . .

As Sandy relates her story, tears well up in her tired eyes. She wonders why she feels down so often, has difficulty concentrating, never has any energy, and asks why she hates her life. She feels as if she's failing because she can't keep up with all the demands being made on her. She believes she is a failure.

I tell her I'd hate my life too, if it was like hers.

She goes on to say that Phil's pouting because they haven't had sex in ten weeks, and he can't understand why she's not interested. He tried to wake her up last night, but she doesn't remember if they actually did the Wild Thing or not because she passed out again within seconds of regaining consciousness.

Sandy thinks if her son starts using Ritalin or a similar medication, all will be solved. Pity it's not that simple. Nevertheless, there are some important changes she can make.

You can too, if you identify with Sandy:

Solutions

Beliefs:

The first thing you need to do is challenge the beliefs you have about yourself and your mom role by answering the following questions:

- Were you really put here on this Earth to be at everyone's beck and call? (What is a beck, anyway?)

- Are you supposed to feel guilty when you don't meet the expectations of others, even though their expectations are unreasonable and unrealistic?

- Should you have to explain, defend, and justify yourself whenever you refuse a request?

- Are you the parent or are you the child, being told what to do by your demanding ADHD kid?

- If you don't control every detail of family life, will the world come to a screeching halt?

- Can you tell the difference between motherhood and indentured servitude?

- Do you feel personally responsible for every single thing that goes wrong in your family's life?

If you don't like the answers you've come up with, that might be a hint that some of your basic beliefs about motherhood need to change.

How do you start making these changes?

Delegate:

Delegating means you have to start making *direct requests* for help, along with a stated expectation that the help will be given. You have to spell out to the rest of the family that you've been shouldering more than your fair share of the burden and that you're no longer willing to this.

Naturally, the family won't like the idea too much, having operated on the principle of "Why bark if you have a dog?"

With your refusal to be everyone's maid/cook/laundry service/personal trainer/social director they'll eventually get the idea that the free ride is over. They'll also be mad as hell, and immediately try to bring about a *changeback reaction.* But if you stick to your guns, they'll have no other choice but to start pulling their own weight.

It's at this point that I usually start getting angry phone calls from crazed kids and even a few husbands. I knew I was making progress with one family when the thirteen-year old son glared at me and said, "Ever since my mom's been seeing you for counseling she's been possessed by demons!"

Support:

As the mother of an ADHD kid, have you ever felt alone? Of course you have, but your experience is not unique—there are plenty of other moms out there, some of whom have gone through what you're going through right now, examples to show you that there's hope, and that there's more to life than cleaning up other people's messes.

There is so much relief in discovering that it's not just you or your kid, that you're not making stuff up in your head. Plenty of other moms have felt the exact same way.

So why are you just sitting there reading this book? Go out and find these other moms! Talk with them, ask what they did to succeed, and ask how they coped, what strategies worked for them, which ones didn't?

Okay, so where do you find support? Contact your local CH.A.D.D. (Children and Adults with Attention Deficit Disorder, a national organization), 499 Northwest 70th Avenue, Suite 308, Plantation, FL 33317, (954) 587 3700, Fax: (954) 587 4599.

Call the Learning Disabilities Association (412) 341-1515 or your local LDA Affiliate. The St. Louis LDA is particularly effective in helping parents of ADHD kids as well as those with learning disabilities (Call (314) 966-3088 if you live in the St. Louis Metro area).

Your local school, counseling office or community directory may also know of support groups.

Even finding one other parent with an ADHD child can make all the difference in helping you break the isolation and frustration you feel. You can learn that you don't have to be micromanaging the entire Universe.

Mom Role #2: The Diplomat

Perhaps you find yourself in the role of diplomat. All family negotiations, acts of war, and peace treaties are conducted through you. You've become the intermediary between your son and husband, mainly because any time they try to deal with each other directly, a fight breaks out. Not that they keep butting heads because they're so alike, or anything like that . . .

You spend much of your time trying to persuade, cajole, beg, bribe, and blackmail Junior into behaving because any time he acts out, Dad does too.

On the flip side, any requests Junior has to clear with Dad always end up coming to you first, because he believes you'll sweeten the deal. Certainly, there may have been times when this approach worked, but overall, playing the Diplomat puts you in an upside down triangle with you at the bottom apex, feeling increasing pressure from the two points above you. A precarious position, because if you don't negotiate properly, you'll find yourself being attacked from both points on the triangle—"You always take Dad's side!" or "You let that kid away with murder!"

Ever wonder why you feel like you just can't win?

Or perhaps you're in the Diplomat role between your child and school, in which case, you spend half your life defending and protecting your little darling from the Psychotic Teacher from Hell. Of course, said psycho teacher sees your kid as the Psychotic Child from Hell, and you're caught in the middle, again and again.

If you are in the Diplomat role, I'd suggest that like your Micromanaging counterpart, you've been taking on more than your fair share of responsibility, which allows the rest of your family, especially your ADHD kid, to be less responsible.

You need to disengage from the Diplomat triangle. Ha! Sounds easy, doesn't it? That's like saying to an alcoholic, "Hey, quit drinking and everything will be fine." Sure, that's true, but there's more to sobriety than not taking that first drink.

So how do you disengage from the triangle?

Solutions

- Recognize that you really are in a triangle as a sort of communications traffic cop, usually because you think there are no other options available.

- Force your kid to make direct requests of Dad and not come through you. In our home, if one of our two teenagers comes to me and says, "Hey, Parental Unit, (I swear that's what they call us) can I spend the night at Lurch's house?" my reply is, "If you've cleared this with the other parental unit." The kids know that dealing with one parent is like dealing with both, the Reciprocal Law of Parenting.

- Any time a wife/mother feels like she's doing 70 percent or 80 percent of the parenting, that means her spouse is only doing 30 percent or 20 percent. Insist that your husband learn how to deal with your kid directly without overreacting, burying his head in the sand or dragging you into an unhealthy triangle.

Disengaging is simply making others do their fair share, that's all. This isn't anything you should feel guilty about, and no, it doesn't mean you're being selfish—breaking the triangle is about fairness and undoing unhealthy family dynamics. When you do break out of your Diplomat role, expect other family members to guilt you, and say how selfish you are. Ignore them!

Enabling:

To take responsibility for someone else who is perfectly capable is called *enabling*. You're enabling them to be irresponsible, allowing them to expect free rides. I understand you thinking that if *you* don't do A, B, or C, it won't get done, but you know, sometimes that's the only way your kid's going to learn.

You want him to improve his grades or not flunk the quarter? Doing all his homework for him isn't going to help in the long run. A mom told me recently that the only reason she writes all her son's term papers is because she really likes typing. Yeah, right!

Enabling simply teaches him how to manipulate others into doing what he doesn't feel like doing for himself. This creates an "Attitude of Entitlement," a belief that the world owes him. Doesn't teach him anything about how to survive in the world or be self-sufficient.

Anyway, you've probably already graduated high school, so why do you need a second high school diploma?

Mom Role #3: The Blessed Martyr

I hate being so blunt, but sometimes martyrs can be a real pain to be around. However, with a little compassion and understanding, you can see how easily a mom turns into a martyr. Most of the time, she doesn't even realize that she's become a Blessed Martyr.

Symptoms of martyrhood include:

- Sighs constantly
- Carries the weight of the world on her shoulders
- Says "Woe is me!" frequently
- Major luggage under the eyes from lack of sleep
- Thinks her life is worthless
- Is angry when others don't pity her
- Tells the kid he's causing her a heart attack/stroke
- Prays for death to come quick in the night

This lady is depressed. The bottom line is she feels like a victim, and acts as if she's helpless, the brunt of Fate's big joke.

Every suggestion that someone puts forth to help, including the good ones, is shot down in flames. Taking responsibility and making change doesn't come easily—feeling trapped and immobile does, which quickly develops into a miserable way of life for the Blessed Martyr.

By the way, if reading this makes you angry, that suggests you might be a . . . nah, never mind, you're probably not. But let's assume you know *someone* who is a Blessed Martyr. First off, you need to treat her the way the

Micromanager has to treat her own kids—by not rescuing and doing everything for her.

One of the root problems is that the Blessed Martyr's kid seized control of the family years ago. She wasn't firm enough when he was younger, a problem further compounded by perhaps a somewhat less-than-involved husband. In a two-parent family, if Dad isn't emotionally present, he may be giving silent permission for the kid to act out with Mom, safe in the knowledge that Dad is not really a force to be reckoned with.

If the kid has this kind of power by age twelve, imagine what he'll be like by the time he's sixteen!

Solutions

- Reclaim your parental power and authority. This requires that you and your husband clean up your own acts first, so get yourselves into counseling and start dealing with any problems between you with regard to parenting and discipline. Undermining your own authority by being a victim and martyr won't accomplish anything.

- Now that you and your husband can present a united front, it's time to take charge of your home. This won't be easy (like living the way you do is?). If you look at thousands of years of history, no individual or group with power has ever given it back voluntarily—power always has to be taken, and believe me, he's not going to give it back willingly. You must display a united front and act with confidence and firm decisiveness.

- Do not spend thousands of dollars on the psychic hotline. You know all that stuff Madame Zephonia tells you? She makes it up! Every time! She's probably got untreated severe ADHD and is entertaining the hell out of herself telling all those lies you pay her to tell you!

- If you are a single parent, the same principles apply. Okay, ask yourself this question, who's the parent? *You!* Who's the kid? *Him!* But you've got to start believing it or he'll simply laugh in your face, making you feel trapped all over again. So get into counseling with a counselor who understands these dynamics, and find a support system.

A Blessed Martyr might reply, "But I can't afford counseling."

This may very well be a valid point, but can you afford to live with such frustration and sadness on an on-going basis especially if you've been unable to bring about change? We're talking about costs—the cost of counseling and medication versus the cost of living in a chaotic, tense, sometimes hostile environment in which you feel out of control more days than not.

Some counselors offer sliding scales, where the fees are set by how much you earn; there are state-funded programs all across the country; there are numerous support groups. It's all a question of deciding what your most pressing needs are, and then finding out how you access these services.

The roles of Micromanager, Diplomat, and Blessed Martyr are not necessarily set in stone. You may experience a combination of all three at different times. Naming and recognizing these roles provides you with a framework from which to begin the process of change. You can't change something if you don't know what you're dealing with.

And now having become familiar with Mom roles, let's move on and talk about Dad roles in the next chapter.

Chapter 7

Dads:

The Good, the Bad, and the Ugly

Thankfully, most of the dads I work with are the good guys. They're open to learning, they're willing to make changes, and are eager to improve the family situation.

These are the guys who are willing to be part of the solution, and often include the following two types of dads:

- **ADHD DADS:** Untreated versions of their ADHD children. Usually decent guys, but end up driving everyone around them nuts.

- **FRUSTRATED-OUT-THEIR-GOURDS-DADS:** Concerned fathers who have done everything they can to help their ADHD kids, but so far, nothing seems to have worked. Many of them have male-pattern baldness.

Unfortunately, there are also other types of dads who are part of the problem instead of the solution, typically appearing in three different disguises:

1. **OSTRICH DADS:** Fathers who bury their heads in the sand in an attempt to ignore problems.

2. **DISNEYLAND DADS:** Often divorced, these guys are into bribery, and want to be their kid's "friend," as a way of not taking responsibility.

3. **PASSIVE-AGGRESSIVE DADS:** Seemingly "nice guys" who really aren't so nice.

However, these three not-so-helpful dads are often unaware that they're not up to speed in the dad department. Nevertheless, if they want to see improvement in their kids, they need to start taking their paternal responsibilities more seriously.

Ostrich Dads

These are the guys for whom the lights are on but no one's home; the workaholics, the alcoholics, the sports fanatics, all of whom may be physically present, but aren't realistically involved in their kids' lives.

Frequently, we find the Ostrich Dad married to a Micromanaging Mom. To be fair, he doesn't *need* to be too involved because Mom takes care of everything all by herself. Dad, like the kids, sees Mom as nothing more than a control freak/busybody, using this as an excuse to make himself scarce, oblivious to what's going on around him as in the following example:

Missy is ironing with one hand and stirring soup on the stove with her other. She has the cordless phone tucked under her chin talking to her son's school principal, while Roger, the Ostrich Dad, is watching basketball on ESPN—

> Missy hangs up the phone and says, "That was
> Mrs.Taylor, Jimmy's principal."
> "You see that slam-dunk? Man!"
> "Jimmy told his math teacher to go have sex with
> a goat."
> "What a shot!"
> Missy slams her hand down on the ironing board.
> "Roger! Are you listening to me?"
> "Yeah, something about Jimmy and goats. What? A
> school trip to the petting zoo? Jeez, look at that
> rebound!"

Missy's blood pressure rises, and there's a tightness in her chest. Through clenched teeth she explains the seriousness of the situation, a three-day out of school suspension.

Roger barely glances over at her and mumbles, "Yeah, I guess he was kinda outta line. That mouth of his will get him in trouble some day. Hey, you see that assist?" he says, and returns to his 32-inch Loony Lantern screen.

What Roger fails to realize, or rather, *refuses* to realize, is that not only is his kid in trouble again, but a three-day out of school suspension not only affects little Jimmy but the entire family as both parents work. Jimmy, their highly impulsive fourteen-year-old, will be home alone. Roger has no clue how potentially dangerous this may be, not to mention that Missy has to figure out all the logistics to ensure Jimmy doesn't burn the house down/raid the liquor cabinet/smoke pot, or engage in any other disturbing home-alone activity.

Both Missy and Roger need counseling and parenting education, lots of it, with an emphasis on Roger learning how to become a more directly involved parent. He'll need to change several of his established beliefs about parenting and family life, one of which is that he believes parenting is mostly Mom's job while he gets to take a back seat.

Unlearning these beliefs can be difficult, and even painful in some cases, but any change in this direction will be an improvement.

So how do you go about dealing with an Ostrich Dad without falling into the role of Micromanager?

Solutions

- Stop managing everything by yourself

- Quit doing so much and even allow things to fall apart, insisting that he pick up the slack

- Don't allow him off the hook with lame excuses

- Let him directly feel the effects of your kid's difficulties by demanding he show up for parent/teacher conferences, taking your kid to the doctor, and reviewing report cards with him

- Increase his anxiety about what's happening to your kid instead of protecting him from it

- When he says "What are we supposed to do with this kid? What do you want from me?" simply say to him, "Counseling."

Mom needs to recognize that Dad's limited involvement is *not* normal and *not* acceptable. Without intervention, things will only get worse for the entire family.

Disneyland Dads

Although Disneyland Dads are a common divorce phenomenon, they also show up in married couples. However, for our purposes, we'll concentrate on the divorce scenario.

Typically, Mom has physical custody, and Dad has the kids every other weekend. Although Mom *now* sees herself as a single parent, in all likelihood she was a single parent even when she was married, as most of the parenting fell on her shoulders because Dad had his work, his customers, his golf, his buddies, and that was about the extent of his life. Oh, and there were a couple of kids thrown in there, too.

Then suddenly (or at least, that was how it seemed to him), she filed for divorce.

At the weekend, Dad takes the kids. They go to lunch on Saturday, the baseball game, the mall to buy toys, videos, movies, bowling, the ice-cream stand, one, big, Disneyland whirl.

Not having strong skills in the parenting department, and perhaps feeling residual guilt about the divorce, he indulges their every whim, and doesn't say no or discipline the kids.

Two reasons why he might refuse to discipline are:

a) personal inadequacy (doesn't want the kids to dislike him)

b) allows them to be out of control as a way to get back at Mom

Naturally, the kids milk this for all it's worth.

If their ADHD kid has already been diagnosed, and is using Ritalin or some other ADHD medication, Dad may "forget" to give it to him, creating further behavioral problems for himself, the kid, and Mom.

Any structure, which their ADHD kid relies on, vanishes completely, and by the time he's dropped off at Mom's on Sunday evening, the kid is a hyper basket case. Mom feels like she's back at square one again. (That's because she is!)

When Mom tries to restore structure and routine, she's immediately seen as the Big Bad Wolf, the nag, the parental nasty, taking all the fun out of life.

Game, set, and match to dad.

Solutions

- Explain to your child simply and clearly what the behavioral expectations are when he is at home with you. Explain that even though Dad permits certain behaviors at *his* home, they will not be permitted in Mom's home.

- Communicate these expectations to Dad. Of course, that might be difficult, but let him know, without yelling or complaining, that the current, inconsistent system of parenting only confuses your child. Emphasize your child's needs, not so much your own.

- If direct communication is impossible, communicate through a trained third party like a counselor, mutually trusted friend or relative, or counseling-trained priest/minister/rabbi.

- Instead of nagging, lecturing, and berating, ask questions, making use of the word "*we*"—"What do you think *we* can do to help Billy control his mouth?" (Duct tape is an unacceptable answer.) "Do you think structure helps?" "What kind of routine do you think *we* can come up with so there is consistency?" "How do you think *we* can teach him to be more organized?" "Have you ever noticed that when *we* give in to him, he seems to become more demanding?"

- Do not cross-examine like you're a trial lawyer! Ask questions that keep the focus on your kid's behavior and best interests. Don't make accusations. People tend to be less defensive, and may even actually think about what you're asking if they don't feel like they're being guilted or put on the spot.

- Always refer to the fact that *we* have to help *our* child, despite the differences between us.

- When your kid comes home and has a hard time making the transition from Dad's "no rules" to your rules, have him take a shower as a way to detox him. This is a symbolic ritual which helps a number of kids adjust to changing homes.

- Model healthy behavior for your kid by keeping your anger and frustration in check, and demonstrating appropriate ways to express it.

Another antidote for the Disneyland Dad syndrome is for you to do more fun activities with the kids, but not in a competitive way. I know, I know, you don't have enough time, but a little up-front time investment can save you tons of wasted time further down the line.

Of course, some teenagers would rather die than be seen in public with their moms, but if you keep at it, they may actually grace you with their presence. An additional side effect from such an outing is that you both might enjoy your time together, a rare occurrence these days, and he might even get to experience you as a real live person instead of a nagging mom. Dad no longer is the only one who is fun to be around. Makes for a nice change for you, too, not feeling like you always have to be the "bad guy."

I realize none of this is easy, but neither are any other methods you've tried, so what do you have to lose?

Passive-Aggressive Dads

Passive-aggressive Dads (PADs) are tricky. They usually seem like such "nice guys," especially in public, but in private, there's a whole other side to them.

A number of PADs are what we term *narcissistic*, from the Greek myth about Narcissus, the guy who turned into a plant. Oops! Wrong story, I meant the guy who fell in love with his own reflection.

To narcissists, appearances and impressing people are everything, as you can see from the attention they lavish on their appearance—never a hair out of place, expensive designer clothes (even if they can't afford them) and a polished smile for everyone. Except you.

Narcissism is often an attempt to bolster a damaged self-esteem, the result of childhood psychological trauma. As a father, the narcissist projects his own wished-for perfection onto his little boy, seeing him as the perfect image he always wanted to be himself. When he finds out his kid has an imperfection, he is silently enraged, or even not so silently, lashing out at anyone who would dare suggest his kid has problems.

He may become more upset if Mom tries to get help for their as yet undiagnosed son. By taking him to counseling or the pediatrician, she is publicly calling attention to his imperfection and "defects."

For a PAD, even the very term, "Attention Deficit Disorder," (especially those last two words) makes him cringe with embarrassment and shame, like he, the Perfect One, had a hand in creating an imperfect child.

Denial, or refusal to see reality, is an understatement for the passive-aggressive/narcissistic dad. In the worst cases, not only does he deny the existence of the ADHD, he may actively campaign against it, resulting in him sabotaging treatment, but frequently in a seemingly "innocent" way such as the following:

- "Forgets" to give the kid his medication
- Covers for him when he does something wrong
- Sets up an unholy alliance with the kid
- Implies Mom is kind of crazy
- Encourages the kid to act out against Mom
- Says the clinician is a quack (might be true)
- Pulls the kid out of counseling, usually citing financial woes even though he's pulling in $200,000 per year.
- Ignores inappropriate behavior and refuses to discipline
- Gives 30,000 reasons why Ritalin and other medications cause cancer and blindness,
- Gives other reasons for discontinuing treatment like counselors are just out to get your money, the kid's just an All-American Boy, you read too many of those damned self-help books, Rush Limbaugh says there's no such thing as ADHD

For making him look bad, the PAD's resentment reaches the point whereby he sets about actively punishing his spouse. Sometimes the punishing may be at an unconscious level, but the PAD is usually aware of *some* anger, which instead of being expressed in a healthy manner, is expressed via the subtle put-downs of his passive-aggressive behavior.

In more severe cases, he forms an unholy alliance with his kid against Mom, undermining her authority with comments like, "Your mother doesn't want you to do that," implying that, "It would be okay with me, but you know what she's like."

Usually when confronted about this undermining behavior and attitude, the PAD gives an innocent, "Who, me?" look, accompanied by a show of hurt and anger that you could even *think* such a thing.

If you're dealing with a PAD, the following solutions may be helpful:

Solutions

- If you feel like you're being undermined, and your child's behavior is deteriorating, then you probably are. Trust your instincts.

- Confront your spouse in a non-aggressive manner, using the following formula, known as the Four Part Assertive Message: "When you . . . (describe the behavior) I feel . . . (describe how you feel) because . . . (say why). What I need from you is. . . (state your need)." This helps remove you from a blaming/accusing position and helps you communicate much more directly.

- Educate, educate, educate

- Seek counseling

- Run away and join a circus/run off with Fabio

Okay, having railed on the problem dads, let's switch gears and take a look at the good guys who bring their own well-intentioned set of problems to the ADHD family.

ADHD Dads

As I mentioned earlier, there are a significant number of ADHD kids whose dads also have ADHD.

Most of these dads were never diagnosed in childhood because unless they were absolute maniacs and fit the old hyper stereotype, no one realized they had ADHD; we just didn't know enough about the condition twenty or thirty years ago.

Like the passive-aggressive dad, the ADHD dad may turn a blind eye to a number of inappropriate behaviors, primarily because he doesn't see why certain behaviors are inappropriate in the first place. He engaged in those behaviors when he was a boy and saw nothing wrong with them. He may still engage in them today! Nevertheless, he really is a good man, just a little misguided, that's all.

Examples of ADHD dad behaviors include:

- Forgets to give Junior his medication
- Spends a ton of money he can't account for
- Has moments of obvious hyperactivity
- Constantly forgets to pay bills on time
- Is impulsive
- Changes hobbies and interests the way most of us change socks
- Never listens

- During counseling sessions (if he remembers to show up) he stares out the window
- Keeps changing jobs
- Has tendencies toward gambling
- Owns a Formula One racing car or is into skydiving

During a recent family counseling session, in which we were discussing a thirteen-year-old's "attraction to danger" behavior, I looked over at Dad and said, "Do you think your son's behavior resembles yours in any ways?"

Out the corner of my eye, I saw Mom nod her head vigorously because she'd been trying to convince him of this for years but he would never listen.

Deciding whether or not Dad had ADHD was tricky, because as an adult, he'd found a number of adaptive behaviors to help him compensate. Initially, he didn't appear like a textbook example the way his son did, but there was still a discernible, subtle pattern of *restlessness, impulsivity,* and *distractibility* running through his life, despite all his compensatory behaviors.

When I approached him with the idea that he, too, may be suffering from ADHD, he was defensive, almost hostile. But the more we talked, the more he was able to see that, well, maybe there were too many behavioral and attitudinal similarities to ignore.

One of the reasons he gave for denying the possibility stemmed from guilt, that somehow he was to blame for his kid struggling in school. I pointed out that if he, as a dad, learned how to deal with his own ADHD, he'd be in a strong position to help his child by example.

On another occasion, I remember a mother in my office who cried with relief for twenty minutes because for the first time in living memory, there was no screaming in the home as both her husband and son were in treatment, using medication, and making significant behavioral changes.

The reason there had been so much yelling was that father and son were so much alike. Any time the kid did something dumb or impulsive, the dad lost it because he was seeing, yet again, another snapshot of himself, which sent him into a tailspin.

Dad's pet peeves were:

That kid never listens
Doesn't follow through
Never does his homework on time
Always late for school

Interestingly enough, Dad was on probation at work after his supervisor filed the following complaints:

Doesn't listen
Lack of follow through
Never turns in paperwork on time
Always late for work

With counseling, education, and treatment, Dad was able to see not only his own ADHD behaviors, but also why his son's were so irritating to him. As a result of treatment, he developed a dramatic rise in patience and tolerance.

As a father, it can be difficult to accept that sometimes you and your kid share certain behavioral similarities. What's even more difficult is acknowledging that maybe your wife has been right all these years, that you really do have ADHD!

If you suspect that *you* might be an ADHD Dad, you might want to take a look at the following suggestions:

Solutions

- Educate yourself as much as possible about ADHD in adults and understand that it's not just a kid condition
- Talk with a counselor who's knowledgeable
- Don't be so defensive
- Always look for the positive
- Join an adult ADHD support group

Your average ADHD Dad has spent a lifetime trying to compensate to living with ADHD, even though he's usually unaware that's what he's been dealing with. To suddenly discover that he might have a "disorder" can be scary and threatening, one of the reasons I advocate a gentle approach. At the same time, most of the ADHD dads I've worked with begin to not only feel relief that there really is a reason for why they act the way they do, but now they can actually do something about it!

Frustrated Out-Their-Gourds-Dads

Like motherhood, fatherhood is not easy, and many dads I work with are frustrated out their gourds by their ADHD sons and daughters. Why on earth can't these kids just do what needs to be done and get on with it? It all seems so simple! But as we know, *nothing* is ever that simple.

We dads are a somewhat simplistic bunch, using rather primitive approaches to many of life's complications, like watching sports, drinking beer, pretending we know how to fix things, and just being, you know, regular dads. All we want is some peace and quiet, and the TV remote control. Only problem is you have an ADHD kid on your hands, so you can kiss your delusion about peace and quiet goodbye, not to mention wasting half your life searching for the remote control.

Now, some of us think all we need to do is watch even more sports, buy bigger power tools, and drink more beer, but you know what, some of us have tried that and it doesn't work too well.

So that means we're kind of stuck with what is. As my very wise father-in-law, Bill Schnarr, often says, "What should be, what ought to be, and what is, are three very different things."

So, fellow Dad, how do you handle your hyper or daydreaming kid without having to consume vast quantities of beer, overdose on ESPN, or spend every waking moment of your life hiding out at work?

For one thing, I suspect that if some of us are constantly frustrated, that's a sign we we're still standing on the sidelines about what's really going on with our kids. That's because many of us have a "natural" tendency to leave those kinds of details to our wives, seeing as how God gave her so much more than us in the parenting department.

So what's a frustrated dad to do?

Solutions

Educate Yourself:

If you're unsure about how to solve a problem at work, I bet you'll do anything to find the solution. You'll talk to colleagues, bosses, read up on journals, surf the 'Net, and discuss it with anyone who might have the solution. Right? (I'm giving you the benefit of the doubt here—most of us begin by trying to ignore the problem.) So why not use the same principles and apply them to your kid's ADHD? (Educate yourself, I mean, not ignore the problems.) Talk with other dads who know about ADHD. Of course, this won't be easy, seeing as how we don't like to admit in front of another guy that there's a problem with our kid. Men in general aren't too predisposed to talking about this kind of stuff.

One time, a colleague and I tried to run a therapy group for men (misguided idiots that we were). There were only three rules; you couldn't talk about work, sports, or sex. Funnily enough, the group didn't last very long, if you catch my drift.

If you're not comfortable talking with other dads, read. Read everything you can get your hands on about ADHD. If you don't like to read, use the audio tape versions of ADHD books, and listen to them on your Sony Walkman while you're doing dad things like mowing the lawn (because Junior has finally won that battle). Or cruise the Internet, making sure you stay away from the sports web pages and those . . . other "distracting" pages.

Become More Involved:

We also have a tendency to get caught up in our work. When we do come home, we may then (naï ve fools that we are) expect to have a meaningful conversation with our kids at some point in the evening.

Does the following scenario sound familiar?

You: "Hey, Bud. How was school?"
Kid: "I dunno."
You: "Learn anything new?"
Kid: "I dunno."
You: "You do your homework yet?"
Kid: "Sure."
You: "You want me to go over it with you?"
Kid: "Yeah, right. Whatever."
You: "Okay. How'd you do on that test today?"
Kid: "Test? What test?"
You: "Gee, sometimes I get the feeling you don't like talking to me."
Kid: "Whatever. Can you loan me ten bucks?"

And you wonder why you're so frustrated? We haven't even come to the part about why he was suspended this afternoon, or why he received an "F" in every subject.

The point is, asking the same questions about how he's doing in school doesn't really give you much access to his private world, the one you're increasingly excluded from.

However, there is one way to increase your odds of entering the Teenage Forbidden Zone, and that is for you to increase your coolness.

In case you haven't noticed, we dads are pretty boring and uncool. How do you find out how cool you are? Take the Coolness for Teenagers Test and find out:

1. Who is Marylin Manson? (Hint: not a girl)
2. Who is Trent Reznor?
3. Who is Jenny McCarthy?
4. Why does he like Jenny McCarthy?
5. Who is Crusty?
6. Who is Homer? (Not the Greek guy)
7. Does a T-shirt with the word "Tool" on the front refer to Tim Allen's show, "Home Improvement?"
8. Does Smashing Pumpkins refer to Halloween?

If you can't correctly answer at least half of these questions, then you're, like, tragically uncool, dude.

And I'm not giving you the answers, either. If you really want them, go ask your kid, which is my point. Find out who *really* influences him.

Instead of asking, "How's school?" day after day, ask if he thinks Beck is cool or is just a big dork. (Don't know who Beck is? Ask your kid.) Implying you know who said Beck person is will blow his mind so much he may even start talking to you!

Make sure you spend time with him, even if it's not the top of his priority list. Find something you both might be interested in (except Jenny McCarthy because that will make your wife angry with you).

Be a Decent Role Model:

One of the reasons we have so many weird kids in our society is that there aren't enough good male role models to show them about *true* manhood, as opposed to the little boys in adult disguises who pretend to be men.

I often ask the kids I see at the office who their role models are, and just as often I'm met with the same reply, "What do you mean?"

More than half of them are making up the rules of what it means to be a man as they go along (like we didn't?), using some of the characters in the above-mentioned pop quiz as models. At least *we* had real men like John Wayne and Superman!

That's *your* role, to show what it means to be an adult, not some bizzarro rock star's who worships the devil. Reclaim your role, your position as Most Important Role Model.

Let's face it, isn't that the essence of Dadhood?

For any dad of an ADHD kid, one of the most important goals is for him to become fully involved in his kid's life, and to step back and examine his parenting beliefs and styles.

As dads, we have to lead the way, set good examples, and demonstrate maturity and responsibility. If we don't, how on earth can we expect our ADHD kids to do so? The buck truly stops here.

Chapter 8

The Golden Child and Other Siblings

Leo Tolstoy nailed certain family dynamics on the head with the opening lines of *Anna Karenina* when he said, "All happy families are like one another; each unhappy family is unhappy in its own way. Everything was in confusion in the Oblonsky household."

Kind of like your household, too, with kids running around in a million different directions, demanding this, crying about that, and so on.

In the ADHD world, we tend to focus so much on the ADHD kid that we sometimes gloss over the other kids in the family. Make no mistake, siblings are acutely affected by their ADHD family member, often developing specific roles and personality traits as a result.

Actually, these roles develop in most families to one extent or another but they may be exaggerated in the ADHD family if there is constant chaos and turmoil.

The Golden Child

He tends to be your eldest and often *doesn't* have ADHD. However, if he does, then the gildedness falls to the second child. And remember I'm generalizing, here—there are no hard and fast rules. To keep things simple for our example, the Golden Child in this instance is a first-born male called Dick.

The next child is Harry, Dick's annoying younger brother. He's the one with ADHD, the Hyperactive-Impulsive Type. His behavior is the opposite of Dick's. Dick does not like Harry too much, and Harry in turn, *hates* Dick with unbridled passion for being a goody-two-shoes Golden Boy.

As a Golden Boy, Dick's attributes include the following:

- Popular
- Responsible
- Successful, academically and athletically
- Strong social skills
- Personal attractiveness
- Empties the trash without being asked
- Mows the lawn (all of it) without being asked
- Never late for curfew
- Keeps his room neat and tidy

I know you might be thinking this kid is everyone's dream, but I'm not so sure. In fact, as I write about this guy, I'm coming to the conclusion there's something really wrong here! Come on, a teenager who keeps his room neat and tidy? It's almost sick! (Or maybe I'm jealous.)

I do concede the point that many Golden Children are a parent's dream. They go off to medical school, marry Little Susie Homemaker, and live happily ever after (even though their obsessive-compulsiveness and perfectionism eventually drives everyone crazy). They often become surgeons, good surgeons. Or accountants. Sometimes engineers. Or other guys who like rules and procedures.

Unlike Harry, the younger brother, who believes to the core of his being that rules were, indeed, made to be broken (assuming he even acknowledges there are any rules).

When Harry first heard me refer to Dick as "Golden Boy," his eyes lit up with instant recognition. (He's not alone, either. All the other ADHD kids react the same way when I refer to their successful brothers and sisters as "Golden Boy" or "Golden Girl.")

Growing up, your ADHD kid *hated* Golden Boy! Imagine living in the shadow of this greatness (my younger sister, Izzy, thinks I was a Golden Boy, but she's delusional—I never kept my room neat and tidy).

And while Dick seems to be perfect, at least from outward appearances, what you don't see is the growing resentment he feels toward Harry because the family often fails to give Dick the attention and recognition he truly deserves. They're too busy dealing with all the problems created by Harry to notice Dick's many accomplishments.

Without even realizing it, you've set Dick up as the standard bearer for the family, and God help him if he ever falls from his golden perch! You may not even have noticed how much you take his achievements for granted. Or maybe you downplay his success because you know Harry feels like a schmuck most of the time, and heaping praise upon Dick will only make Harry feel worse about himself.

As long as Dick continues to do his job as Golden Boy, everyone is happy. But this can lead to increasing parental expectations that are both unrealistic and unfair.

Harry can shove the cat into the microwave for his Science Fair project, and you roll your eyes, yell a little, maybe even sing a couple of Barry Manilow numbers to punish him, but, well, that's just the way Harry is, right?

Dick, on the other hand, said a bad word when Harry backed the riding lawnmower over his foot, and you yelled at him for two hours about how you expect him to show a better example for his younger brother, even though younger brother Harry just fried the cat!

All Dick said was "Damn," and now he feels like you're treating him like an ax murderer! As a result, Dick is not only angry, he's hurt, and feels seething resentment toward Harry *and* you. But naturally, being a Golden Boy, he hides these negative feelings from everyone. After all, he's got a reputation to uphold, he's the good guy, Mr. Perfect, always lending a hand and being super responsible.

These scenarios can set up a peculiar dynamic I've seen in Golden Children which I refer to as *Kamikazeism*. Strange as it may sound, your Golden Child may start screwing up deliberately, like coming home from a party bombed out of his mind, or getting an "F" on a no-brainer test at school, stymieing everyone who knows him.

Deliberately dive-bombing his gilded reputation happens for three reasons:

1. As a protest about being taken for granted
2. Curious about how a "normal" kid feels
3. Burn-out from constantly being held up to such high standards

Kamikazeing occurs because your expectations are too high. You've come to expect nothing short of perfection, and if he gives you anything less, he's going to hear about it in no uncertain terms. Well, you know what? Golden Boy is going to screw up anyway because he's human just like you and me.

So when he does, in the words of the TV philosopher Bart Simpson, "Don't have a cow, man!"

As one seventeen-year-old Golden Girl said to me recently, "There's not much room to maneuver on a pedestal."

If you have a Golden Boy or a Golden Girl in your family who's in danger of becoming a kamikaze, what can you do?

Solutions

- Re-evaluate your expectations and make sure they're realistic
- Reward accomplishment
- Don't neglect him due to an ADHD sibling's crises
- Don't put him on a pedestal
- Allow him to make mistakes
- Lighten up when he does make a mistake

You need to let him know how much you appreciate his efforts and success. Talk openly about how you're not taking him or his accomplishments for granted. So often, Golden Children come to think they're only worthwhile because of their accomplishments. Make sure you get the point across that *who* they are is more important than what they *do!*

Acknowledge that you may have neglected him because you've been so caught up in his ADHD sibling's hell raising, and that you're trying to make changes.

Your Golden Child needs to be educated about ADHD just as much as you do. Explain that the ADHD kid acts like a maniac for a specific reason, not just to steal attention from the Golden Child.

The more family members who understand exactly what they're dealing with, the faster change will be brought about in the family.

The Invisible Child

Let's say Dick is out winning new sports trophies because Harry used the old ones for target practice with his BB gun.

Where's your youngest and only girl, Debbie? Lost in the shuffle, that's where, minding her own business, being all sweetness and light, but for the most part, invisible.

She resents both Dick and Harry with an intensity that borders on a mania, but she keeps these feelings to herself. She resents Dick because he struts around like a self-appointed second father instead of a brother, and she resents Harry because he ties her up and locks her in the closet or shoots the heads off her Barbie dolls with his BB gun.

Unfortunately, she resents Mom and Dad even more because she feels deprived of your attention thanks to you spending all your time putting out the forest fires created by Harry. When you're not on fire-fighter duty, you're up at Dick's high school to watch him receive another award.

So, every so often Debbie will just whack Harry on the head, then cry bitterly that he started it because she's angry with you but doesn't know how to tell you. Over the years, she's learned from Harry that negative attention is better than no attention, so she goes ahead and thwocks him again. He hits her back. She yells. *Now* she has your attention.

But once this mini-crisis passes, Harry's grounded, the family goes back to its familiar dysfunctional dance, and she becomes invisible again.

Because she's lost in the shuffle, you need to reach in and pull her out. You must keep her from melting into invisibility, now, before it's too late. If you don't, she'll develop problems with assertiveness, social skills, and self-confidence.

Teach her how to use her voice, how to be assertive, how not to live in the shadow of someone else's greatness or screw-ups. If you don't, you're setting her up to be a victim.

Solutions

- Acknowledge to her that she has, indeed, been lost in the shuffle

- Spend one-on-one time with her

- Include her as much as possible

- Reassure her she does actually exist

- Give her a voice

- Ask her opinions

- Listen to her

Don't just sit there and wait, hoping she'll grow out of her invisibility—she won't. She needs your attention right now.

If you do wait, one day she'll start dating a leather and chain-clad youth with an impressive array of body piercings and a plethora of exquisite tattoos. I'll bet she'll get your attention then!

Or how will you react when you discover she's on a date with her 457, 899th married man in a desperate attempt to have someone pay attention to her?

See why I'm suggesting you deal with her invisibility now and not later? She needs your attention, *now!*

The Scapegoat

The Scapegoat is your ADHD child, Harry, who certainly isn't as cute and demure as his invisible sister (if you can find her) and he most definitely can't compete with Golden Boy, Dick, even if he wanted to.

Whenever Harry went anywhere, following the hallowed footsteps of Dick, he would hear comments like, "Hard to believe you're Dick's brother," "Why can't you be more like Dick?" "Dick was such a *successful* student!" and "Your mother must wonder where you came from." (Harry's inevitable reply to that last comment was usually something like, "She had a fling with the heating repair man.")

Studying the origin of the word *scapegoat* tells us something about his role. The word is mentioned in the Old Testament, Leviticus 16:8, *"A goat upon whose head are symbolically placed the sins of the people after which it is sent into the wilderness in the biblical ceremony of Yom Kippur."* Webster's Dictionary defines scapegoat as *"a) one that bears the blame for others, and b) one that is the object of irrational hostility."*

Harry, via his ADHD HIT behavior, has entrenched himself in the role of scapegoat. Everyone knows it, everyone's used to it, and everyone has come to expect it, especially Harry.

If you stumble upon a bunch of kids getting up to mischief, and you ask who the ringleader is, you'll hear an instant chorus of "Harry! He told us to do it!"

Harry is so used to being blamed, yet so tired of always being in trouble, he immediately becomes defensive, and shoots his big mouth off when you confront him.

His defensiveness, hostility, and the fact that he's coming unglued right before your very eyes tells you he must be guilty as charged.

The problem is that he really *didn't* do anything wrong, but now you're mad at him simply because he acted like such a little jerk when you confronted him.

This kind of scapegoating happens to him all the time.

For example, Invisible Debbie, his seven-year-old sister, thwocks him on the side of the head with a shoe. Naturally, Harry thwocks her back, twice as hard. Little Miss Innocent, tears gushing down her face, screams at the top of her lungs, "Harry thwocked me with a shoe!"

You run into the room see her bawling, and there's Harry standing there with a shoe in his hand, an angry look on his face.

The more he protests that she started it, that he was only defending himself, the angrier you get, and he's grounded for a million years. He sulks, feels hurt and manipulated, but who's going to believe him?

The incident further reinforces his belief that the world is out to get him, and nobody cares and nobody understands. He becomes even angrier and more sullen, acts out his frustration by kicking the dog, and is punished yet again.

By the time Harry is fifteen-years-old, is it any great mystery why he's a sullen, angry-looking kid with a "bad attitude?"

He has "successfully" tied himself up in scapegoat knots, sees no way out, so who cares anymore?

Many of the scapegoats I know really don't like being in the scapegoat role, but they can't see any way out. In a sense, it's been thrust on them by a combination of neurobiology, personality traits, family dynamics, and environmental factors.

In my own case, one of the main ways the scapegoat role showed itself was because I could never shut my big mouth, not even when I tried. One fateful day in 1971, when I was in sixth grade, my inability to stop talking actually caused me to be officially condemned to burn in the fires of Hell for eternity, as you'll see from the following almost-true story:

In Scottish Catholic grade schools in the late 60's, one of the ways the church raised money for foreign missions was by introducing a fund-raising system known as the Holy Childhood Society, a similar system to the American "Pagan Babies" program whereby if kids contributed enough money to fill a milk carton with a picture of a Pagan Baby on the side, they could "adopt" said Pagan Baby, unbeknownst to Pagan Baby's family.

In the Scottish version, if we contributed our allowance and met the designated financial target, we were rewarded with a photograph of a sad-looking Biafran child with a blank line underneath his image so we could baptize him with a good New Testament name like Matthew, Mark, Luke, or John. This was taken Very Seriously. Any not taking this Very Seriously might result in eternal damnation.

So I got to thinking that pretty soon all the kids in the Biafran village were going to be confused what with them all having the same name.

When I tried to imagine the pagan babies, I'd see a bunch of once-heathen kids running up to their friend's thatched hut and knocking on the door:

"Hey, John, you seen John?"
"Yeah, he's over at John's."
"The John next door?"
"Nah, his cousin John's."
"Oh, that John."
"Yeah, that John, John."

Way too confusing. So I decided to help them out and start changing the names. I wasn't trying to be a smart-alec, wasn't trying to make trouble, I was just trying to be helpful, that's all.

The first batch of names I came up with were Albert Einstein, Napoleon Solo, Clark Kent, Roy Rogers, James Bond, and Dean Martin.

Okay, I'll be honest, I knew this was against The Rules, but all those other names were *so* boring. And even though somewhere in the back of my mind I knew I'd get caught, well, I guess I really didn't think much about the consequences. I knew that one day, Albert Einstein and Dean Martin from the Biafran village would thank me.

The idea soon spread, and we all giggled and chuckled like this was the funniest thing in the world. But to my horror, an unforeseen side-effect was that we'd boosted our class financial contributions so much that the Archbishop was coming to thank us personally!

On the day of his visit, I feigned a variety of diseases, tried to make myself barf, hyper-ventilated, begged, pleaded, offered money, anything to get out of school, but nothing worked.

"You're going, young man, and that's that!" my mother explained tenderly.

We sat in class solemnly, hands clasped in front of us on the desk while our teacher, Mrs. Danforth, asked us to present our baptized babies to the Archbishop.

No one moved as he sat there prince-like in a specially raised chair upholstered in cracked red leather. The chair creaked like a rusted door-hinge any time he shifted his immense weight. He was a sight to behold, all decked out in a black cassock and a purple sash, a matching purple beanie on his bulldog head.

He frowned, his thick gray eyebrows gathering like approaching thunderheads. I figured the beanie must be too tight on his head. He coughed impatiently, but still no one moved.

Slowly and accusingly, all the other kids turned to look at me because I was the one who'd started this naming craze. Mrs. Danforth followed their gaze in my direction, and she looked at me suspiciously, a look I knew all too well.

Unable to take the growing tension any more, I jumped right out of my seat, and thrust about twenty or so Pagan Baby pictures at his Blessedness.

Slowly, and I mean slowly, he read out the names, "Albert Einstein, Sophia Loren, St. Sebastian the Pogo-sticker, John Wayne . . ."

His Worshipfulness thrust a meaty finger in my face. "You, boy, are a cynic, and cynics burn in hell!"

A sink? What was he talking about, I wondered.

He looked down the length of his bulbous nose, a big red one like Rudolf the Reindeer's. There were tiny red spider veins on the surface. He glared at me, and said, "What do you think you're doing, boy?"

I tried to swallow but my mouth felt like cotton. "How do you mean, your Blessedness."

He rolled his eyes. "Your Grace," he sighed loudly.

"My Grace?"

"Don't be foolish, child! You are to address me as your Grace, you ignoramus."

Ignoramus? That was a Latin word. Mmm . . . "I'm sorry," I said, and studied the white scuffmarks on the toes of my shoes.

"As well you should be. What are you doing here anyway, in this school funded by Holy Mother Church?" he growled.

"Uh, learning stuff." The thunderclouds gathered in his face again. Oh, God, I was about to die. To get on his good side I had to think fast. The Latin, I'd use Latin. After all, he was an Archbishop. I'd show him I knew some of his language.

"You're learning *stuff*? Tell me, what *stuff* have you learned, apart from insolence?"

"Latin, your . . ." I forgot how to address him! "Your Grateful Blessedness."

His thin, dried-out lips curled into a faint smile and he steepled his fingers. "Very well, say something in Latin."

I gulped. The only Latin I'd ever learned was from my dad, an electrician who for some bizarre reason was obsessed with the language. Most of what he'd taught me was funny, nothing sacred or classical, but it was my only shot. "I can say anything?" I asked, double-checking.

"Hurry up, foolish boy!"

Okay, okay. I took a deep breath. "Semper ubi, sub ubi."

The Archbishop's nostrils flared. He shot a furious look toward Mrs. Danforth. "Did you teach him that?" he demanded, his episcopal jowls jiggling with indignation.

She scurried toward his Blessedness. "I'm not quite sure what he said, your Grace."

The Archbishop tugged her cardigan sleeve, and pulled her closer, never taking his narrowing eyes off mine for a second. He whispered to her, "This idiot said, 'Always where, under where!'"

"Always wear underwear?" she asked, turning pale.

The Archbishop dismissed her with an imperious wave of his hand, then turned his attention back to me. "Enough of this fiasco! What do you think I should do, boy?"

Every time I opened my mouth with this guy, the hole I was digging for myself got deeper. I pursed my lips, willing myself not to speak, but this made him even angrier.

"I asked you what I should do, boy," he bellowed.

"Uh . . . about the pagan babies or the underwear?"

"The pagan babies, you damn fool child!" he yelled, waving his hand threateningly close to my flushed face. His large episcopal ruby ring flashed by my eyes. "I want an answer!" he demanded.

I stared at the giant ruby on his finger, and suddenly had another of my "brilliant" ideas that would surely save me. It all made perfect sense! I closed my eyes and thought, Don't speak, Don't speak, Don't . . . "I think you should sell that whopping big ring, your Warship. Imagine how many pagan babies you could buy for *that!*" I said, the words tumbling out of my mouth all by themselves.

Apparently, that was the wrong answer.

I knew I was supposed to shut my mouth, so I did, but it had made him angry. He asked me to speak, I did, and now

look what happened! In-school suspension, a billion deten-
tions, shamed, grounded by my parents, and worst of all,
condemned to eternal damnation for being abusive to his
Blessedness!

Ten-years old and I was going to burn in hell forever!
What a bummer! Then I swore another oath that I'd never
speak again. Of course, this only lasted about thirty seconds,
then I started yakking on about something else.

As you can see, this was clearly scapegoat behavior, no
question, but it wasn't malicious per se. More like thought-
lessness and impulsivity of the mouth, you know, the same
kind of thing you see with your own scapegoat kid.

Okay, so what can you do about your scapegoat? Bring
him to my office to have him "fixed" or "cured" and everything will be fine? I think not!

One time a married couple dropped off their fifteen-year-
old scapegoat in the waiting room for his first counseling session while they went off to "Bits-O-Dead Cow" restaurant,
leaving word with Jasmine, our receptionist, that they'd be
back in an hour to pick him up. All I had to do was wave my
magic wand over his head and he'd be cured. Not exactly
what you'd call "involved parenting."

Their behavior and attitude spoke volumes as to why the
kid had a slightly negative attitude. In fact, I won't work with
a child unless the family is involved in counseling to some
extent. If I only work with the scapegoat and he makes
changes but the rest of the family doesn't, he's just been set
up to fail.

In Family Systems Theory, the scapegoat kid is known as
the IP (Identified Patient). *He's* the problem, we're all fine,
thank you very much. If a kid enters counseling as an IP,
don't expect him to be cooperative. The idea of counseling

merely furthers his belief that he's the family screw-up, and that once again, everyone's picking on him.

The best way to approach counseling is as a family, whereby you acknowledge that everyone has a part in the family chaos, not just the scapegoat.

Solutions

- Take note of how many times you automatically assume your kid will live up to your scapegoat expectations (you may be surprised at the frequency)

- Explain to your kid the concept of scapegoat and the IP in detail so that he knows what he's dealing with

- Stop inadvertently setting him up to continue the self-fulfilling prophecy

- Break your knee-jerk scapegoating reaction when he does screw up or make a mistake

- Reassure him that he isn't single-handedly responsible for *every* problem in the family

- Demonstrate this by ensuring the whole family makes use of counseling

Classroom Scapegoats

Scapegoat roles have their uses. In a classroom setting, an ineffective teacher can use a scapegoat's acting-out behavior and trouble-making reputation to hide her inability to keep order. If there's any disruption in class, you can be sure to find our little scapegoat Harry somewhere in the middle of the action, allowing the teacher to justify her chaotic classroom. "How can anyone have an orderly class with Harry raising hell all the time?" she asks with genuine innocence.

And all the other teachers nod in sympathy, thanking God they don't have Hyper Harry in *their* classroom.

Another situation in which a scapegoat role serves a useful purpose is when the *teacher* has undiagnosed ADHD. My experience has been that in these situations, the ADHD kid instinctively knows how to push every wrong button on the teacher, and both teacher and kid go after each other with a vengeance, battling it out like two little kids in the school yard.

An eleven-year-old ADHD boy can reduce a thirty-nine-year-old teacher with ADHD down to his level in a matter of seconds:

Teacher: "You think I can't control you? Watch me!"
Harry: "Watch you what?"
Teacher: "You behave or else?"
Harry: "No, you behave."
Teacher: "I'm warning you."
Harry: "Bite me!"
Teacher: "Go to the office!"
Harry: "Make me."

On and on they go, a relentless hurricane blowing through the class on a daily basis, sweeping up in its path resource room teachers, principals, parents, counselors, and entire school districts, not to mention the other kids who are supposed to be receiving an education.

Parents hear from teachers, "Your kid's out of control."

Teachers hear from parents, "You're mean to my kid."

Either way, Harry gets nailed. So to help Harry *and* his teacher, there must be counseling intervention. One of the first things I do is to meet with Harry's teacher.

I also like to make sure the principal has an idea of what's going on because astute principals are often helpful in resolving these problems (but only if they're made aware of what's going on inside the classroom).

If it appears that Harry's teacher possibly does have ADHD, when I meet with her individually again, I'll try to help her recognize her ADHD symptoms, and will eventually make a referral to a local competent professional for an evaluation. (I can't do the evaluation myself as I'm already working with her in a different context.)

She may have been able to function all these years without anyone recognizing she was dealing with ADHD, but there's no way she'd ever get past an ADHD kid!

I remember one kid like Harry who said to me right in front of his teacher, "See? I told you he was just like me!"

The more a scapegoat kid knows about his role, the easier it is for him to stop perpetuating the cycle of always being in trouble. Believe it or not, most scapegoats don't really like their role. Despite their devil-may-care attitude, they get tired of always being in the hot seat, especially it they weren't deliberately trying to cause trouble.

For example, one of my major unwitting scapegoat moments was on Palm Sunday, 1975, when I single-handedly caused countless souls to remain in Purgatory for an extra year.

At the Mass of the Passion of the Cross in boarding school, the entire Gospel story of Jesus' crucifixion was read by one of the priests, the *long* version, which took about twenty minutes. There was a time-honored tradition that if you stood motionless during the reading, you freed a soul from Purgatory.

I tried not to move, I really did, until I heard a loud buzzing near my head. Instinctively, I jerked my head around to find the source of this ominous sound. Suddenly, I felt a wasp land on my neck! I don't know which was louder—the sound of my hand slapping my neck, or the collective shocked gasp of the congregation.

The priest who was reading paused for a few seconds, then glared at me with a look of disgust as if to say, "Oh, that's just great. You've caused all those souls to suffer the fires of Purgatory for a whole other year, you moron!"

And they wondered why I was developing a "bad" attitude! Not only were the priests mad at me, there were now a bunch of dead guys mad at me, too!

They all thought I had done it deliberately, just to be a troublemaker, but that wasn't the case. That's why it's so important to teach your kid about his role. Only when he's learned specifics can he go about changing his behavior.

Sibling ADHD

What if you've spent so much time and energy putting out your scapegoat's fires that you haven't noticed that one of your other kids has ADHD, too?

If you've spent years dealing with a kid who has obvious ADHD HIT, it's easy to miss the fact that one of your other kids has ADHD PIT, the Inattentive Type, because over the years you've come to associate ADHD with hyperactivity and impulsivity.

The thought of having another ADHD kid might have been too much to contemplate, so you didn't quite notice that he was quietly slipping through the educational system. And now you're puzzled because he's starting to flunk tests and his grades are dropping. You figure he's just immature, a late developer, generally disorganized, and has been feeling the stress of his ADHD HIT brother's constant crises. So when an astute teacher mentions that your quiet kid seems to spend an awful lot of time daydreaming, you think, "What? You're telling me he's got ADHD, too? I don't believe this!"

Cursing under your breath, you take him for an evaluation, just in case, and to your dismay the clinician does, indeed, make a diagnosis of ADHD PIT. The only problem is that your kid refuses to accept he has ADHD despite the evidence.

Like you, he has come to associate ADHD with his hyper maniac brother. He says to you, "There's no way I even come close to acting like Mental Marty! What kind of stunt are you people trying to pull? Do you see ADHD everywhere you look? You guys are obsessed!"

How do we convince him? The first step is to teach him about the different types of ADHD, and show him how his own specific type is different from Marty's.

Having been reassured that he's not turning into his hyper brother, he'll soon discover there are easier ways to manage his life, improve his grades, and become more competent and successful.

Remember, ADHD is a vastly complex condition with three distinct species (four if you count ADHD NOS). It's easy to miss in other family members if their symptoms aren't too obvious.

Of course, you could argue that if their symptoms aren't too obvious, then why bother treating it in the first place?

Two answers:

a) with time and the increasing demands of life, the symptoms will worsen

b) I've never dealt with anyone, not even with a mild case, who said, "Damn! I wish I'd never received treatment.

Sibling Role Switching

Some of you may already have seen this happen—you have a Golden Boy, Dan, and his ADHD scapegoat brother, Jeremy, who's been in counseling for six months.

Jeremy has been working hard in counseling, uses his medication, follows through with responsibilities, has started turning in assignments, and has been improving his social skills. He's stopped telling his teacher she's a two-bagger (one who is so ugly that putting a single paper bag over her head isn't enough), actually does his homework, and no longer brings his whoopee cushion to church during services.

So now you think, Great! I have a new Golden Boy, and you start showering praise and reward on Jeremy, Golden Boy Number 2 (GB2).

But GB1, Dan, feels threatened. You're stealing his gold stars and accolade, and giving them to his little jerk brother, who's just conning all of you anyway.

Being a tad perfectionistic, Dan doesn't handle any of this too well. He's frustrated and angry (although he keeps it to himself, of course), and then to everyone's amazement, he flunks math, his favorite subject! GB1 gets his first "F" ever.

To make matters worse, GB2, the upstart Pretender to the Throne, is gloating over Dan's failure. GB2 now works even harder at getting positive attention, not to mention how good he feels that he's finally becoming successful while his archenemy is turning into a complete loser!

How can this be? Just when you thought everything would be wonderful, GB1 starts turning into a scapegoat right before your very eyes! The more successful GB2 is, the more angry and self-sabotaging GB No.1 becomes!

Solutions

- Spell out to both kids, openly and honestly, the potential danger of role-switching. Reassure GB1 there's enough praise to go around, that praise and reward are not in limited supply

- Use the terms "GB1 and GB2" when talking to them as a mildly humorous way of reducing the growing tension between them

- Teach your new Golden Boy (GB2) how to enjoy his hard-won success without gloating and trying to set up his former rival

- Don't neglect GB1 and don't take his frequent accomplishments for granted

Conclusion

All family roles—Golden Child, Invisible Child or Scapegoat Child—become so easily ingrained, especially if the roles serve multiple purposes for the family.

Changing the roles of your kids requires understanding which dynamics are at work. Role changing requires commitment and effort on everyone's part, which is why I emphasize the importance of the whole family entering counseling and not just your scapegoat.

Naturally, the *non*-scapegoat kids will object, "Why do I need to see a dorky counselor? I'm the good kid. I don't act like loony Hyper Harry, for crying out loud!"

Doesn't matter, whether they recognize it or not, they, just like you, have been affected by Hyper Harry's ADHD in some way, and they, too, need to grace us with their presence in the counseling office.

Some of their resistance may stem from not fully understanding the whole picture and from having bought into a number of the common myths surrounding ADHD, which conveniently enough, is the subject of our next chapter, *Fact or Fiction: ADHD Myths*.

Chapter 9

Fact or Fiction: ADHD Myths

I always swore I'd never write a self-help book, mainly because so many people told me I should, and the quickest way to get me to *not* do something is to tell me I *should*.

But I caved in and started writing anyway. One of my primary motivations is that I'm bothered by how much garbage and misinformation is floating around out there about ADHD, misinformation distributed by Flavor-of-the-Month talk shows and tabloids which scream headlines about ADHD medication causing cancer and drug addiction.

Mainstream media has done a fairly decent job of covering the subject of ADHD, especially *Time* magazine and *Newsweek*, but that doesn't change the fact that there are other publications out there which only present the negative aspects of ADHD.

One out-of-town newspaper reporter harassed me for months, begging me to let him interview all my ADHD clients, the ones who are dope dealers in the Ritalin trade, even though I don't see any who fit that description. The kids I work with who use Ritalin, Adderall, and Cylert don't abuse their medication as far as I know, simply because they find so much benefit from using it as prescribed. Okay, there is some evidence that a percentage of druggie kids sell Ritalin on the street, known as "Vitamin-R" but I don't know any of them personally. All the dopers I work with smoke pot and trip on acid; they don't take Ritalin (although a number of them should).

Can you imagine the headlines if they did? "National Epidemic of Kids Not Acting Out, Studying, Reading, and Doing Homework. President Declares State of Emergency!"

This reporter still calls occasionally. He's kind of obsessive, talks too much and too fast, makes inappropriate comments, taps his pen against the phone mouthpiece, and always interrupts. Mm, I wonder . . .

The point is we have to separate fact from fiction, myth from reality. The following are a sample of popular myths about ADHD:

MYTH #1   *"If your kid has ADHD, he'll end up in jail for murder, maybe even become a serial killer."*

There's no escaping the fact that a high percentage of ADHD'ers with the hyperactive-impulsive type (HIT) are in prison due to crimes associated with high levels of impulsivity: "Yeah, your Honor, encasing that guy in concrete just seemed like such a good idea at the time, ha ha. And what with me having ADHD and all, I just couldn't resist the impulse."

If you look at the ADHD population in the prison system, you'll find few inmates with a *single* diagnosis; more often than not they have dual or triple diagnoses as they tend to come from violent, abusive backgrounds, with some alcoholism/drug abuse thrown in the mix.

I've treated hundreds of ADHD'ers with hyperactive-impulsive type, but to my knowledge, none of them are doing time. Of course, that's not to say one or two of them might not end up in the pokey one day, but for the moment, I think we're free and clear.

Still, this is a hard myth to get beyond. A couple of years ago, I watched an "Oprah" show during which she interviewed a young man in prison via satellite link. He'd stabbed his girlfriend forty-something times.

Oprah said, "Why? Why did you do that?"

His answer? "I have ADHD."

See how this one works—"I have ADHD, therefore I stab people who really, really tick me off."

MYTH #2 *"If my kid uses Ritalin, he'll become a drug addict."*

I doubt it. My experience with ADHD kids has been quite the opposite. Many undiagnosed, untreated kids are drawn to stimulants like speed, amphetamines, and cocaine in an instinctive, yet misguided attempt at self-medication. Instead of being all revved up when taking these drugs, they usually calm down, become focused, and experience a general sense of well being. They might even pay some bills or do a few crosswords.

If these kids receive intervention early enough, there is no need for attempts at self-medication. At the same time, we can't be naï ve and think that ADHD kids who are treated with medication never do drugs. But there's plenty of research indicating that appropriate medication intervention can decrease the tendency toward drug addiction.

MYTH #3 *"How can my kid have ADHD? He sits in front of that Nintendo for hours!"*

Aha! Maybe be the biggest myth of all—if he's hyperactive, how come I see him motionless, focusing, and concentrating so intently?

ADHD is a condition replete with paradox (like when we give speed to a hyper kid, he calms down). Well, one of the paradoxes is called "hyperfocus." All of us, ADHD or not, have the ability to become absorbed by activities we enjoy. For many ADHD kids, however, this absorption is greatly magnified, like when a hyper, distractible kid suddenly calms down instantly when you sit him in front of a computer screen or video game.

MYTH #4 *"ADHD means you're dumb or retarded."*

Nonsense. Most of the ADHD kids and adults I've met have been bright, highly creative, and demonstrate clear streaks of genius in their own way. If you rely solely on report cards and grades, sure, many of them appear less than intelligent with all those "D"s and "F"s but who ever said our educational system worked well for these kinds of minds?

Our current system is more suited for linear thinkers, those highly structured, organized, motivated individuals, with inherent math/science biases. These people then go on to become scientists, teachers, bankers, engineers, and all those math types, like my accountant. One of the reasons he likes math and numbers is because they are absolute, incontrovertible. For him, $2 + 2$ always $= 4$, it's a given, undeniable.

One of the reasons I drive him crazy is that for me, $2 + 2$

can be whatever I need it to be, depending on the situation. To all you left-brained, math-oriented people, this statement is crazy, but to a right-brained, circular-thinking, creative type, well, if it suits our purposes. . .

I also have the backing of a tax attorney I know who says 2 + 2 can, indeed, be whatever you need it to be. His parole hearing is set for 2004.

ADHD'ers are not dumb or stupid, but they certainly do think differently, processing information using a variety of unorthodox methods.

MYTH #5 *"ADHD doesn't even exist."*

Neither does the IRS. Nor does depression. And like depression, ADHD doesn't necessarily show up with obvious physical symptoms. But just because there are no in-your-face physical symptoms doesn't mean the condition doesn't exist.

On PET scans, the brains of ADHD'ers show up differently than non-ADHD'ers, revealing differences in metabolic activity. There are some skeptics, of course, who say we touched up the photographs to convince the public of our agenda. They're the same people who believe in the New World Order, see black helicopters, are abducted by Men in Black, and tell us that at any minute, UN troops are going to declare martial law in the United States. They also watch too many episodes of "The X-Files."

MYTH #6   *"He just needs to pull himself up by his boot-straps."*

No, he doesn't, he needs treatment for ADHD. If I hear this one once, I hear it a thousand times. First of all, if he could pull himself up by his bootstraps, don't you think he eventually would? You think he likes running around feeling like a loser with trashed self-esteem, the Resource Room King? Certainly, he may tell you he likes living this way, but he's lying through his teeth!

I remember one young ADHD client, Brad, who was repeatedly told to try harder by his high school teachers. Brad admitted that he wasn't exactly putting forth 100 percent effort, so after another go around of "D"s and "F"s he decided to try harder. He got up early every morning, studied as hard as he could for the tests, asked for additional help, forced himself not to pass out during math class, and paid attention in history class.

When he came to see me, he was upset. "You know what I got? A lousy "D"! They lied! They said all you have to do is try harder, and I did, and look what happened! They said pull yourself up by your bootstraps but nothing changed!"

Pulling himself up by the bootstraps was not the issue for Brad; lack of motivation was. He wasn't motivated because he saw himself as a loser, so that even when he did study, his heart wasn't in it. A word or two of encouragement would have been more effective as he had so many doubts about himself and his academic abilities.

These myths and others like them come from lack of accurate information. You need to get the facts for yourself, and not just rely on hearsay and speculation, otherwise you'll continue to perpetuate the misinformation, which won't help you or your kid.

And by the way, the next time you want to yell at your kid about picking himself up by the old bootstraps, try a word or two of encouragement instead, and watch what happens.

Chapter 10

ADHD in the Classroom: Parent Perspectives

As Charles Dickens once said, "There are good parents, and there are not so good parents, good teachers and some real yahoos, good schools and educational goat sheds."

What if your kid is in one of those "goat sheds," a place where they don't seem to have a clue about education or kids in general? How will you know?

Well, first off, he'll probably tell you outright. However, you might not take his complaints too seriously, as he doesn't have too much going for him in the credibility department, having been known to exaggerate ever so slightly. He doesn't exactly demonstrate what you'd call a pro-education attitude, either.

Nevertheless, if you do hear the same complaints over and over, and they don't just sound like his usual carping about how awful school is, and how he hates having to go, then you might want to investigate a little further.

Complaints can be listed on a graduated scale from Mild, Moderate, to Severe:

- "My teacher hates me!" *(Mild)*
- "If I look the wrong way, I'm busted."
- "She says I'll end up flipping hamburgers."

- "The other kids get away with everything."
- "The teacher calls me a loser." *(Moderate)*
- "She calls me stupid in front of the class."
- "I'm not going to school."
- "I'm not getting out of bed." *(Severe)*
- "I feel such hatred toward my teacher."
- "I cannot tell a lie—it was me who tried to burn the school to the ground."
- "I hope he gets hit by a bus."

Needless to say, if you keep hearing these kinds of comments, and you really believe they aren't simply his usual whining, then most likely there's a problem at school.

But before we go any further, I want to emphasize that this chapter is not about teacher bashing or school-scapegoating—it's about addressing common school problems which arise for ADHD kids and their parents.

Lack of Understanding

Teachers don't know everything. Counselors don't know everything. No one knows everything (except teenagers).

Some teachers know a lot about ADHD. Others don't know much, and there's even a whole bunch who refuse to acknowledge its existence, like Ms. Brown in the following almost-true story:

I was working with a thirteen-year-old boy, Jimmy, who had ADHD HIT, a diagnosis his mother tried to explain to his teacher at a local private school. Unfortunately, Jimmy's teacher, Ms. Brown, refused to listen to his Mom.

Meanwhile, the tension between Jimmy and his teacher increased. Mom tried calling the principal but she wouldn't listen either, viewing Mom as a trouble-maker and boat-rocker, one of those pain-in-the-butt parents who always makes excuses for her kid.

Frustrated, Mom asked me if I would call the school. I agreed, but was never connected with the teacher. I left several messages on her voice mail, none of which were returned. Then I sent a letter asking if she would call me when it was convenient. No reply. Nothing.

Meanwhile, Jimmy would give me status reports of the war between him and his teacher. One time he even tried to explain his diagnosis to her himself but not surprisingly, she blew him off with a comment about ADHD being a figment of our imaginations.

Watching Jimmy's grades plummet (along with his self-esteem), I decided my only option was another letter, written in a way I hoped would get her attention:

Dear Ms. Brown:

I have been unsuccessful in contacting you regarding the situation between Jimmy Smith and yourself.

As you won't speak with his mother or me directly, we are unsure of how much of what he tells us is true.

His latest comments were that you said, "ADHD is a figment of our imaginations." Although Jimmy does occasionally do his homework, I agree there have been times when he has not turned in the assignments. I am also aware he has a tendency to speak out and engage in attention-seeking behavior when he does not receive enough structure or guidance, all of which suggests ADHD-type behavior.

But assuming you are correct and ADHD *is* a figment of my imagination, my only diagnostic conclusion is as follows:

Jimmy likes attention, therefore he appreciates when you point out to the rest of the class that he is three sandwiches short of a picnic.

He spends every Sunday evening thinking of ways to annoy you on Monday morning because you always wear blue on Mondays and Jimmy hates blue. He believes you wear blue because you hate him.

When he shoots his mouth off, even though he knows he'll receive a detention, it's because he secretly wishes to be sent to the principal's office, primarily because she does not wear blue on Mondays.

He especially likes the fact that the other kids call him a social retard, an idea reinforced by your frequent eye rolls any time he does try to make a contribution to the class.

He taps his feet and drums his fingers because he is planning a future career as a drummer/percussionist.

He doesn't always turn in assignments because he enjoys seeing his grades drop, because he has a strong need to feel humble.

He gets up from his chair repeatedly because he has a chronic hemorrhoid problem.

Although in seventh grade, he deliberately chooses to write at a third grade level as he doesn't want to show off to the rest of the class and bring embarrassing praise and accolade about how beautiful his handwriting really is. His cursive is illegible. His printing is legible, but you insist he use cursive in the event he wishes to pursue a career in medicine.

From a clinical perspective, I would suggest that diagnostically, Jimmy is blue phobic, has too much humility, and has delusions of being a drummer/physician.

Sincerely,

The ADHD Counseling Guy

P.S. Maybe try a little beige number next Monday.

Okay, so I exaggerated a little; I suggested she actually wear white next Monday.

The main idea here is that Ms. Brown refuses to acknowledge there is a valid explanation for Jimmy's behavior. Perhaps if she opened her mind a little, she might discover there are ways in which she could make his behavior more manageable in the classroom. But until that happens, the battle will continue, with neither of them winning.

To break the deadlock, Jimmy's mom needs to find at least one ally inside the school—a resource room teacher, a school counselor, anyone who will listen and help make a dent in Ms. Brown's blockheadedness.

Alternatively, Mom can have an independent counselor or pediatrician talk with Ms. Brown to explain that Jimmy's behavior is not simply a personal vendetta against her or vice versa.

The teacher may have any number of reasons why she doesn't understand or isn't willing to learn about ADHD. As a parent, you have to keep hammering away until you get the point across, otherwise the problems between your kid and his teacher will continue to escalate, with your child getting the short end of the stick.

Denial

Along the same lines as lack of understanding is a related phenomenon called denial, plain outright refusal to see or accept reality.

Despite your best efforts at trying to educate teachers about ADHD, they may still not accept its existence. A quote from one particular middle school teacher sums it up perfectly:

"ADHD is nothing but a pathetic excuse for underachieving, lazy, undisciplined, manipulative loser delinquents who've been heaped upon us by bleeding heart liberals who scorn the traditions of excellence in education." No ambiguity here, that's for sure!

The above-mentioned quote is almost verbatim from an eighth grade teacher, "Mr. Smith," who graduated from the Marine-Corps-Commie-Hating-Boot-Camp-School-of-Teaching, after he completed several stints in Southeast Asia.

But you know, to some extent, Old Smithy has a point. In certain educational circles there is a tendency to focus more on self-esteem than actual learning. If we were to meet every individual's learning needs based on their own unique learning style with self-esteem as the main goal, education would be impossible.

The simple truth is that no one is going to change the educational system to fit *every* individual child's needs, including the needs of your average ADHD student. That's why we have to teach these kids how to succeed in the existing system via all sorts of creative and innovative strategies. Like actually doing homework. Or even turning in assignments.

But one of the most effective methods for academic success is to provide the kid with academic accommodations.

Academic Accommodations

Let's say your kid is having learning difficulties in school. I can't speak for other states, but in the St. Louis public school system, the procedure is as follows: Assuming the teachers have noticed there are problems, they will notify the Care Team, a group of educators who deal with struggling kids. If they decide there's enough evidence to suggest your kid is having genuine problems, they recommend academic accommodations, like oral testing or untimed tests. They will then track the child's progress for three or four weeks to see if the accommodations make any difference. If this is the case, the Care Team will then make a recommendation for testing.

However, the St. Louis Special School District who does the testing will not test for ADHD as such, only learning disabilities.

If you have suspicions that your kid does have ADHD, then you may need the testing done by an independent evaluator who will inform the school of the results. Even then, the school may only allow accommodations *if the ADHD truly impacts the child's learning ability.*

Okay, so let's say you and the teachers conclude that his ADHD symptoms are clearly impacting his learning ability. You now have to set up what is known as an IEP (Individualized Education Plan). The IEP is the blueprint for your kid's education plan. In the IEP, you and the school system decide on the most appropriate modifications and accommodations for your kid's ongoing progress and follow all the recommendations.

If the school doesn't follow the IEP, that might cause some problems at an administrative level. Please note: you use the IEP to help your kid, not to hit the school over the head with (unless it's genuinely warranted). Most of the schools I work with are very helpful and accommodating, making excellent use of IEPs.

Of course, you can run into certain teachers who don't agree with the IEP, and drag their feet on the issue. If this happens in St. Louis, you simply contact the Area Coordinator and inform her that the school is "out of compliance" with the IEP. That usually takes care of any problems.

Alternatively, you may invoke Section 504 of the Rehabilitation Act (1973) which states a school system can't discriminate against a student because of a disability. You use the 504 to develop an accommodation plan based on your kid's academic needs.

In some private school settings, things might not run as smoothly as they're not required to follow the same guidelines. But if they receive *any* Federal funding, that's a whole other story because failure to comply with a kid's accommodation needs may, in some cases, threaten the funding. Certainly, a number of private schools offer wonderful accommodations, but the ones that don't, well, you might want to reconsider whether or not your kid might do better at a school that does.

But say your kid is given accommodations. What does this really mean? Simply put, accommodations are an attempt to level the playing field like providing untimed standardized tests or oral testing instead of written.

Why are we so hung up on timed tests anyway? If we define a test as a measurable, quantifiable method for evaluating knowledge and understanding material, why do we need to demonstrate said knowledge in nanoseconds?

As a Licensed Professional Counselor, I have a smidgen of specialized knowledge in counseling (as well as in Ed McBain novels) but the speed at which I produce this knowledge doesn't seem to matter that much to my clients. It's *what* I say, rather than how *fast* I say it that counts. Anyway, being from Glasgow, Scotland, what with my thick accent and all, if I speak too fast, no one has a clue what I'm trying to say in the first place!

Can these accommodations be abused? Absolutely, no question. But that doesn't mean ADHD or LD kids shouldn't have equal opportunity.

So if your ADHD kid needs accommodations, make sure there's an IEP or Section 504 Plan in place, educate yourself and his teachers, and know your rights. Failing that, transfer your kid to another school.

Lack of Structure

Once again, the structure mantra repeats itself. An ADHD kid in a highly unstructured classroom setting will usually experience learning and behavioral difficulties. Yet the teacher and some of the other kids may work best in an unstructured environment. Expecting her to alter her personal teaching style would be unreasonable but you might suggest she put more specific structure on your child.

Explain to your kid that additional structure is not a punishment, but a special technique tailored to fit his unique needs to help him become more successful.

Lack of Communication

Come on, admit it, how many of you freaked when you received this kind of letter two days before the end of your kid's last semester?

Dear Mr. & Mrs. Mullarkey:

Brian is flunking six out of seven subjects, a pattern which has continued since the second week of the semester. He has an "F" in every subject except Health.

Sincerely,
Ms. Johnson

And you stare at the letter in shocked disbelief that for all these months, no one has noticed or even mentioned to you that Brian is in a little academic trouble. Your immediate response is, "What's going on up at that school?"

Your response in itself tells us something, namely, you really *didn't* know what was going on! You *presumed* everything was fine because when you asked Brian how he was doing, he said, "Fine."

And you believed him? Are you nuts? Presuming anything with an ADHD kid is the kiss of death!

In the last chapter on Myths, one myth I didn't cover was the delusional belief that ADHD teenagers will use common sense, you know, things like, "If I have a test due in two days, I guess I really should do a little studying," or "Now that I've actually completed an assignment, I should probably hand it in to the teacher."

Naïvely assuming your ADHD kid will do what needs to be done is not exactly the most effective strategy for school success.

On the teacher's part, she presumes that you, the parent, will know what's been happening, and even mistakenly assume that her Least Favorite Student in the Universe will show you his progress reports. Everyone is presuming and assuming and everyone is dead wrong.

Additionally, having not heard anything from you throughout the semester, the teacher decides that you're one of those parents who aren't really interested in your kid's progress or lack thereof, with the result that none of you realize there are problems until the last week of the semester.

Now you're mad at the teacher, and she's mad at you because you're obviously one of those parents who doesn't care about your kid's education. To add to the mix, Brian is mad at everyone, especially himself, for yet another failure, reinforcing his belief that he really is a dummy after all!

Solutions

- Communicate with his teachers. Inform them he has ADHD and what that means. If they refuse to listen, bonk them on the head. Nah, on second thoughts, please do not, because as you know, that would be illegal, open you to lawsuit, and set a bad example for your child.

- How to communicate includes both of you signing assignment notebooks each day, sending notes to each other, phone calls, conferences, and e-mail. Personally, I've found e-mail to be an effective method to communicate with a number of teachers; otherwise we spend most of our time talking with each other's answering machines.

- Communicate expectations and strategies to your child. Make him an active participant in the communication between home and school. (Make sure he doesn't hide notes or trash them on the way home.)   Let him know communication is about helping make his life easier, not just a punishment or a way to embarrass him.

Amateur Psychology: 101

In an earlier chapter for parents, I quoted the old adage about a little knowledge being dangerous. Same thing applies to teachers. Some of you may have had your child diagnosed by his or her teacher in the following manner:

Dear Mrs. Dingbat:

Your kid is hyper, drives us all nuts, so he must have ADHD. Better load that little sucker up on Ritalin.

Sincerely,
Miss Clueless

Not exactly the recommended approach for a teacher to raise concerns about a child's behavior or lack of progress.

Teachers, no matter how psychologically astute and aware, are not diagnosticians. If they feel a burning desire to engage in psychological testing, they should go back to school and become psychologists, counselors, or physicians.

Nevertheless, there are some good teachers who are, indeed, blessed and gifted with an innate ability to spot specific psychological difficulties a child is experiencing, but these aren't who I'm talking about; I'm referring to the amateur psychologists who start operating outside their designated professional mandate. Nothing seems to anger parents more than an amateur psychologist labeling their kid.

The good guys, the ones who know what they're doing, firmly, yet politely, recommend a referral for an evaluation, rather than suggesting you sprinkle powdered Ritalin on his Cornflakes in the morning. They make you, as a parent, part of a team working toward the best academic interests of your child.

The not-so-good ones approach this slightly differently, "Hey, Mrs. Jones, your kid's a wacko. Can't you drug him or something?"

Although this type of Neanderthal approach is provocative and insulting, she may actually have done you and your kid a favor by bringing problems to your attention. If you hear similar comments from other teachers, too, well, they're probably on to something here. In that case, it might not be a bad idea to take your kid for an evaluation (even though the thought of Ms. Clueless being right kills you!).

Solutions

- Keep the lid on your protective instincts.

- Step back and ask yourself if the teacher has made valid points. When you think about it, the teacher may actually spend more time around your kid than you do (at least during weekdays).

- Even though you think her attitude stinks, try to listen to what she's saying before you decide what action to take.

- Don't argue, just listen, and then seek a professional opinion.

Do communicate and don't be defensive
Do educate but don't be insulting
Do advocate but don't whine
Do listen and don't presume and assume
Do be honest but don't be aggressive
Do be assertive but don't go off half-cocked

Chapter 11

Teachers: How Not to Have
A Nervous Breakdown

Okay, teachers, do you ever wake up in the wee hours of the morning bathed in a cold sweat at the thought of having to deal with that psycho ADHD kid in your class? For some of you, this is no exaggeration. I know of several teachers for whom nightmares and panic attacks were regular occurrences until there were appropriate interventions (they quit teaching and became truck drivers).

In a grade school class of twenty-five students, all it takes is one ADHD HIT kid jumping up and down like an insane jack-in-the-box, encouraged by his giggling friends, to create chaos and mayhem, driving you and the other kids to absolute distraction.

Perhaps you've discussed the situation with your knowledgeable principal, and he or she has given you useful guidance and support. But what do you do if your administration is less than helpful, responding by saying it's your problem, deal with it?

Well, the first thing you do is take it upon yourself to learn new behavioral management techniques (for the kids in class, not the administration because that might be a lost cause).

But before we get to those, let's take a closer look at some behavioral techniques that *don't* work:

- Locking him in a closet
- Tying him up and gagging him
- Slapping him in leather restraints
- Giving him your own stash of Ritalin
- A cattle prod
- Raging like a maniac
- Screaming
- Lecturing
- Crying hysterically

And of course, the reason you can't use any of these techniques is because they're illegal and unethical, even though several of them may have crossed your mind on more than one occasion!

Instead, I refer you to Part B of the Education of the Handicapped Act (as amended by Public Law 94-142, 1990). Adapted from Preassessment Resource Material, Kansas State Department of Education, 1986, and from my own observations and discussions with teachers and Special Ed. Teachers:

Educational

Move seat to another location
Assign preferential seating
Isolate student for short period
Change setting from large group to small group
Consider individual instruction with a peer or adult
Have a note-taking buddy
Set time expectations for completing assignments
Set time limits using a timer

Be flexible with time
Tape lessons so student can listen at home
Simplify vocabulary
Break test down into small segments
Use visual or memory aids, pictures, charts, cartoons
Use highlighters
Use outlines, study guides
Don't overwhelm with huge amounts of material
Teach him how to organize an assignment notebook

Teach the three R's of remembering directions:

Repeat directions exactly
Restate them in his/her own words
Respond by doing what the directions require

Give both oral and visual instructions
Speak slowly
Use short, Anglo-Saxon based words like "house"
instead of Latinate words like "residence."
Use pauses when giving instructions and allow him time
to process information
Permit oral testing
If written test is failed, test orally to see if student knows
the material
Allow students to tape record
Vary lesson presentation, using lectures, small groups,
large groups, audio-visual aids
Peer tutors
Demonstrations, experiments, simulations, games,
one-on-one instruction
Give immediate correction of errors

Ask student to repeat instructions to see if he
understands
Identify student's preferred learning style

Behavioral

Immediate reinforcement for correct response
Explain incorrect behavioral responses
Discuss inappropriate behavior in private
Conference with student's parents
Conference with other teachers
Conference with counselor
Conference with principal
Establish home/school communication system for
monitoring behavior
Post rules and consequences for class behavior
Privileges are contingent upon behavior
List small steps needed to change (Baby steps)
Draw up a student contract
Move closer to student
Make a list of reinforcers
Use tangible reinforcers (points, tokens, stickers) for
appropriate behavior
Activity reinforcers, free time, time on computer
Role play to demonstrate appropriate behavior
Send him to the office with a note which says, "This is a
note."
Have him clean board, water plants, etc.

Don't be afraid to experiment and devise systems which
may better suit you and your student's needs, management
techniques which include the following:

Win-Win Technique

Let's say you're faced with an ADHD HIT kid who's decided to make a career out of driving you crazy. No matter what interventions you use, this particular guy *has* to have the last word, determined to win.

One solution is to employ what we call the "Win-Win Technique." Sit him down, and tell him straight that you know he wants to win, but the reality is he hasn't a chance due to the school system being on your side (hopefully!). Let him know that every time he finds himself in trouble, he's just let you win, yet again. But if *he* wants to win, all he has to do is behave. That's because if he does behave appropriately and you censure him, it's going to make you look real dumb, and all the other kids will see what a moron you are! In other words, if he stays out of trouble, and keeps quiet/stays in his seat/doesn't disturb other kids, then he wins because he's shut you up and got you off his back!

Every kid I've taught this to has taken great delight in getting one over his teacher by behaving!

John, a thirteen-year-old, describes his first attempt at Win-Win: "So I'm sitting quietly, dying to call out the answer, but I don't. Instead, I sit there, hands clasped on the desk thinking, Ha! Look at you! Just waiting to give me a demerit for shouting out loud, and here I am driving you crazy by not saying a word! Go on, nail me! Go ahead and yell at me and make a fool of yourself! I can see her glancing over every few seconds waiting to pounce but I'm not giving her a chance. I love it!"

Jay, a fourteen-year-old ADHD HIT boy from a public school describes the outcome of his early attempts at "Win-Win," as follows:

"Dude, it was *so* cool! There I was sitting still, not opening my mouth, doing all my work, even the boring stuff, and dude, it was like driving her crazy not being able to rip on me! She loves writing a big fat "F" on my paper, so last night, I studied my butt off. Don't tell anyone, but I even asked my dad for help. When I took the test in third hour and passed, she had to give me a "C"! It's making her psycho, dude!"

See why we call this a Win-Win? Not surprisingly, Jay's teacher wasn't too upset about him getting one over her with his new technique.

Creative Behavioral Management

Although structure is a must for ADHD kids in the classroom, repeating the same ineffective techniques that don't even work half the time is a recipe for failure.

As you may have discovered, ADHD kids tend to be highly intuitive, and know exactly how you'll react when they act out, giving them an immediate advantage in any power struggles. Your predictability can even be a liability in these situations, allowing them to be one step ahead of you some of the time.

One method of creative behavioral management is to do the unexpected, responding in an unpredictable manner. I realize being unpredictable goes against current wisdom but there is a place for such strategies when dealing with the ADHD mind. Paradoxically, you still need to need to show some predictability and consistency in your *un*predictability!

As an adjunctive faculty member of St. Louis Community College at Meramec, I was often faced with young ADHD adults, a number of whom required a certain level of creative behavioral management.

I remember one ADHD student named Biff, who, on the first day of class immediately set up a confrontation between us. His behavior became so inappropriate that eventually I had no other choice but to ask him to leave the class, which was exactly what he wanted.

Naturally, he refused, trying to force us up to the next level of the power struggle. I sighed, and he sneered, knowing he had won or soon would, as he believed I'd either start raising my voice, leave the classroom, or make all sorts of inane threats.

Biff did have a point here because my immediate instinct was to say, "Get outta here, you jerk!" but having "been there, done that" in the past, I knew it was a set up. I decided an unexpected response was called for, and remembering a story one of my colleagues had told me of how she'd handled a similar situation, I informed the rest of the class they were now on a break. Instantly, thirty-four student chairs slid back, leaving Biff sitting alone without an audience.

"Bummer," I said quietly.

Biff snarled, muttered expletives under his breath, then stormed out the room, his combat boots clunking loudly on the floor.

When the other students returned, there was no sign of Biff. Not too surprisingly, he dropped the class (Adolescent Psychology) frustrated that I wouldn't play by his rules.

I hadn't behaved in a traditional, predictable manner. If I had, he may have succeeded with his disruptive behavior. But faced with this novel and unexpected response, and having lost his audience, he was unsure of how to handle the situation, and simply gave up in disgust.

Of course, I had taken a chance by using that particular strategy. Biff could have been an ax murderer, and then I wouldn't be here to relate this story, but you know, sometimes, you just have to take risks when applying creative management techniques. Being willing to take risks and leave your comfort zone is what gives you the edge when managing ADHD behavior in the classroom.

A few more examples include:

- If the kid complains about how you teach, have *him* teach the class. You'd be surprised how often this works.

- Start tossing an object up and down in your hand while you're talking. So often this technique takes advantage of the kid's distractibility, and he's so mesmerized, he forgets about the power struggle.

- Be consistent in your unpredictability.

- Experiment with your own techniques.

- Be willing to take risks.

- Don't take acting-out behavior personally.

- Make sure your students know all your expectations in advance.

Managing Problem Parents

Having discussed some techniques for managing the student's behavior in class, what about the other half of the equation, the parents?

As you know, some parents are wonderful to work with, responding openly and willingly to requests for involvement in their child's academic career, but I'm sure you've come up against the other ones, the Problem Parents, who fall into five distinct categories:

1. **The Whiner and Complainer:** You know the one I mean, the mom who whines and cries about how no one ever listens to her as she wrings her hands, rocking to and fro in despair. No matter how many good suggestions you make, she shoots them down, and gives you a million excuses why they won't work.

2. **The Pit Bull:** She crashes into your classroom like a rabid pit bull, ranting and raving about suing you, even though this is only the first time you've actually met face to face. She's going to sue the school, the district, and the factory that made that uncomfortable chair which causes her son to leap up and down during class.

3. **The Snake:** She never addresses concerns directly to you, but sneaks off to the principal with innuendoes and insinuations dripping from her forked tongue, gossiping, sniping, and back-biting

4. **The Chicken Little:** She runs around yelling, "The sky is falling! The sky is falling!" She's always in a panic, making mountains out of molehills, calling you every day with another "crisis."

5. **The Denier:** I bet all of you know this one, "*My* child would never do such a thing. *My* child is picked on. *My* child is being led astray by those delinquents you can't control in your class." (And you bite your tongue trying not to say, "So why don't you take *your* child to another school?")

Okay, so maybe I'm being a little harsh here, but we can't pretend they don't exist. Of course, they may have a few screws loose, but the majority of them aren't malicious; they're just standing on their last nerve, stressed to breaking point, forced to become victims and control freaks from years of living with a particularly difficult child. As a result, they come across as obnoxious, creating all sorts of problems, and in so doing, make it easy for us to scapegoat them. This in turn makes it difficult for us to listen to what they're trying to say and see things from their point of view.

Instead of going after them with a vengeance and taking their complaints personally, I'd recommend you start using the following behavioral management techniques:

1. Use the No.1 strategy that I recommend parents use with uncooperative teachers—educate, educate, educate.

2. Refer them to counseling, but don't start off by saying, "I think you're mental. Better go see a shrink, you obnoxious pain!" This approach does not promote a strong sense of teamwork.

3. Refer them to counseling again, because they've probably not followed through with your last suggestion.

4. Get as much support for yourself as you can from colleagues, principals, and counselors to help you navigate the storm.

5. Don't overreact. Step back and discuss the problem with a supportive colleague or principal before taking any kind of action.

Self-Doubt

Assuming that you've given yourself some breathing room by exerting some behavioral management with the Problem Parents, your next task is to eradicate any doubts about your teaching ability that these parents have planted in your mind. Problem Parents can batter your self-esteem, and shake up your belief in yourself as an educator.

Even though you're constantly barraged by their complaints, if you believe you're doing everything you possibly can to help their child, then you need to accept that you really *are* doing your best. Don't allow Problem Parents to make you feel incompetent.

One of the more common ways Problem Parents can erode your self-esteem and plant doubt is by inviting you to participate in an unconscious psychological game we'll call "Pass-The-Anxiety" (PTA). The PTA game goes as follows: "I'm afraid for my kid, he's out of control, he's acting out all the time, I feel out of control, this is all making me sick with worry and anxiety. Here, teacher, why don't you worry for me? *You* deal with my feelings, go on, take them, take 'em all!"

And quite literally, that's what happens. After meeting with a PTA parent or talking on the phone, you discover that *you're* now feeling anxious and nervous, wondering if maybe the problems are your fault after all, because you really are a lousy teacher. You know this for a fact because the PTA parent told you on several occasions.

Don't play the game! You'll never win because in terms of psychological games, whoever initiates the game always wins! That's just how it works.

Instead of getting hooked into the game, listen to your colleagues, your administration, and your students, all of whom recognize that you are a good and caring teacher. Any time you hear complaints, always consider the source. Repeat after me, "Consider the source." Say it again, "Consider the source."

If after saying this you still keep doubting yourself, it's a sure sign that you're in the PTA game. The best way out of the game is to hand the anxiety back to the parents immediately, because it's *their* anxiety, not yours.

You hand the anxiety back by accepting that you really are doing your best, as evidenced by all the success you and your students have had over the years.

Next thing is to tell yourself that while you acknowledge and understand the parents' frustration and anxiety, you will no longer take them on as your own. Don't get sucked into the vortex of their anxiety tornado. If you see one of these suckers coming at you, step aside, and allow it to blow past you. Don't play the game!

One of the surest ways to defeat yourself and invite burnout when dealing with an ADHD kid and Problem Parents is to feel self-doubt and anxiety on a constant basis. You're the teacher, not the family babysitter and whipping post. Keep that in mind.

In addition to implementing creative management techniques for kids and Problem Parents, you can also make use of a formula called the *Three E's of Education (3E's)*.

The Three E's of Education

The Three E's of Education are *Entertainment, Encouragement*, and *Enthusiasm*.

Entertainment

Okay, I know kids are supposed to be in school to learn, not be entertained, but coming from a culture with the attention span of a gnat, unless there's some kind of entertainment or stimulation, you're quickly going to lose the interest and attention of your students, ADHD or not.

By entertaining students, I don't mean performing a circus act or doing a dog and pony show; I mean generating a high level of interest in the material you're presenting.

All of us know there are teachers out there who know more about a given subject than anyone else in the Universe. The problem is that some of these Einsteins are hopelessly incapable of transmitting their knowledge and understanding to students. Most of the time this is simply because they don't know how to teach in an entertaining or interesting manner. To put it bluntly, they're boring.

Being the most brilliantist in a subject (that was just to see if you were paying attention) doesn't necessarily mean you know how to teach it. The fact that some of these intellectual giants have the personality of oatmeal doesn't help much, either.

Think back to your own childhood and adolescence. Do you remember the teachers who made an impact, your role models, the Great Ones? I bet all of them were able to entertain you to some extent, either with their enthusiasm, drama, flamboyance, and their ability to connect with you as a real live person, not just a snot-nosed kid.

Now think back to your worst teachers—probably about as inspirational and entertaining as drying cement.

In addition to entertainment sustaining interest, it's also an effective behavioral management technique in and of itself. An interested and involved student is unlikely to start acting out, nor is he faced with the same temptation to engage in power struggles. So many power struggles and acting-out behavior have their genesis in plain old boredom. Talking, laughing, yelling, wandering around, making rude noises, arguing, defying and so on, are often simple attempts at self-entertainment to alleviate boredom or frustration.

Entertainment is an effective antidote to academic ennui, not only for your students, but also for you. Let's face it, aren't there days when you feel like you're on automatic pilot, teaching the same old stuff day in and day out? When you increase your Teacher Entertainment Value (TEV), you'll probably experience a renewed interest in what you're teaching, and most importantly, stave off the feelings of stress and burn-out which are the result of academic boredom.

Enthusiasm

If the subject you're teaching is entertaining and stimulating to you, then you'll most likely demonstrate a certain level of enthusiasm. Enthusiasm is contagious, quickly spreading to create an atmosphere of anticipation, learning, and motivation.

My Latin teacher had flamboyant tendencies, and was highly entertaining, but that wasn't the main thing that motivated me; his dynamic enthusiasm and the fact that he treated me like a person with feelings and unique abilities were. His enthusiasm was electric. I'd never have dreamed of taking a nap, stare out the window in his class, or ask stupid questions just to annoy him!

Then there was one of my English teachers who cursed like a sailor! He used a curse word at least once in every class, and we loved every second of it! Here we were in a religious school, and one of the priests said bad words!

During class, we listened intently with great anticipation waiting for that one fleeting moment when he would say, "Bastards!" when referring to literary critics who got on his wrong side or when speaking about the British Government, a major pet peeve of this feisty Irishman. An unorthodox teaching style, but it sure kept my attention.

A word of caution: Before you start cursing at students as a way to promote enthusiasm, I'd strongly suggest you reconsider this course of action. Cursing in a school setting is not advisable and not recommended, especially in today's litigious and politically correct society. That would be rude, to say the least. If you were to say, "Okay, you bunch of @%*%## ! Turn to page twenty-seven of your %#$@%@^!! book, and study the #$@@$^&%$*! passage," you'd certainly get attention, but not the kind you'd really want.

Think on how you project your enthusiasm toward your students. Are there any improvements you can make? Are there any new or innovative ways to present material?

The third of the three E's is Encouragement, a key attribute in motivating students.

Encouragement

If you only criticize and never offer encouragement, you'll end up with a defeated spirit on your hands, and defeated spirits aren't too good at learning.

A prime example is David, a twelve-year-old boy in a private school. He has ADHD CT, with a chronic habit of forgetting assignments and/or not turning them in. He is *highly* disorganized, spends much of his time daydreaming, and emits the occasional rude noise.

His school uses a system of paper slips for academic and behavioral transgressions. For behavioral boo-boos, he receives a red slip, and for academic ones, a blue.

When I first met this sad little boy, he had so many red and blue slips in his book bag he needed an eighteen-wheeler tractor-trailer to carry them all from school to home. (What he's supposed to do with all these slips is anyone's guess.)

When I called his teacher to ask about the mountain of slips David had acquired, she told me they were part of an "encouragement" system. When I mentioned that her system sounded more punitive than motivating, she told me I didn't understand, and insisted that the system is highly effective with all her students. Except for malcontents like David.

This method of "encouragement" reminded me of a segment I watched on a TV newsmagazine a few years ago about a Japanese management technique. If a manager screwed up, he had to wear a "Ribbon of Shame." For each additional mistake, he received another ribbon. Once he reached a certain number of ribbons, he was then banished to Shame School where he could *really* be humiliated for weeks at a time.

I don't wish to impose my own cultural heritage and bias on another culture, but this struck me as an unusual way to offer encouragement and increase motivation.

If we tried this at the local Chrysler plant or at Boeing, I suspect there might be a wee bit of an outcry in some circles. I can just imagine Charlie walking into a bar after work with his Ribbons of Shame:

Bartender: "Hey, Charlie, what's with the 170 pink ribbons stuck to your workshirt?"

Charlie: "Ribbons of Shame, my man. I am an unproductive American auto worker who wears these as a sign of my incompetence and remorse." Looking down, he says, "As you can clearly see, I am truly ashamed."

Union Guy: "Hey, Charlie, can we talk . . ."

Assuming there would, indeed, be an outcry at using the above system as a method of encouragement, why would we think it okay to use with school kids?

Meanwhile, back to David. (Thought I'd forgotten didn't you?) Sitting across from him, I asked if he could remember the last words of encouragement he'd ever heard from his teacher. He gave me a blank look as if he didn't understand the question, so I asked him again.

He looked up to the left, bit his lower lip, and paused for a few more seconds. "3,687 slips ago. I think I was in fourth grade."

"That's a lot of slips."

"I guess," he said, staring at the floor.

"Is that why your parents brought you to see me, because of all those slips?"

He let out a long, long sigh, and his head slumped forward. "Yeah. They say I'm depressed, and I don't care about anything any more. They're upset because I keep telling everyone my teacher sucks."

David was caught in a scapegoat trap. The more slips he was given, the more he acted out, so the more slips he was given. To help him out of the trap, my first counseling strategy was to teach him the Win-Win technique.

After a few sessions, he started making progress. We then added a new feature—every time he "won" by not acting out or by actually completing *and* turning in an assignment, by making use of his very active imagination, he issued his teacher with a giant black paper slip which he stuck on her forehead.

Now motivated by feeling like a winner for the first time, David practiced hard, going for two whole weeks with out receiving either a red or a blue slip. Then he "accidentally" belched loudly the following week and received a red slip, his first in three weeks. But after this minor hiccup, he was back on track.

Meanwhile, his parents and I were trying to work with the principal and the teachers, who hadn't realized how much of a problem the slips had become because none of the other parents had ever complained before. Uh-huh, sure.

The good news was that we finally convinced his teacher to offer him a word or two of genuine encouragement, and David rewarded her by increasing his efforts even further.

Since then he hasn't misbehaved enough to warrant any more slips. And while David and his teacher haven't exactly lived happily ever after, life is so much better for both of them.

Teaching kids of any kind is always a challenge, but teaching a child with ADHD is one of the greatest challenges facing any teacher.

But remember, the challenge doesn't need to wipe you out or cause sleepless nights. Like everything else in life, if you don't understand something, talk with people who do, learn as much as you can, and be willing to take risks.

As an educator, you need to educate yourself before you can truly educate someone else. But you don't have to do it all by yourself. There's plenty of help available there for the asking. So do that, ask!

Meanwhile, see what you can do about implementing or expanding upon the three E's, Entertainment, Enthusiasm, and Encouragement.

Chapter 12

Honestly, Grandma's Pet Wildebeest Really did eat my Homework!

(How to Win the Homework Wars!)

If you think a teacher has a difficult time getting your kid to pay attention and complete assignments, you can imagine (or maybe you've already experienced) how much more difficult it is for a parent.

Many parents with homework-avoiding kids liken the homework struggle to a war zone, each side trying to outflank the other with move and counter-move. They win some, they lose some, but mostly they lose.

You want to win this war? Of course you do, but first you'd better understand what you're truly up against. To find out, you need an insider's view of the Homework Wars.

An insider's view always gives you a strategic advantage, and so to win said advantage, we turn to an insider who has agreed to grant us access to the Forbidden Homework Dodging Zone, a young man I've known for many years. For reasons of confidentiality, I can't use his real name. Instead, he requested I refer to him as Strangelove Malone. (I've no idea why, nor do I wish to because God only knows what he'd tell me!) Anyway, here are ten proven techniques for avoiding homework as used by Strangelove Malone:

1. Forget to bring your books home from school.

2. Play dumb. That's easy 'cause everyone thinks you already are.

3. Jog real fast to make yourself sweat, then pretend you're sick. I saw that on a movie, "The Client." It works pretty good. But don't do it too often or they'll figure out what you're up to.

4. Say you didn't get any homework tonight.

5. Say you already did it in studyhall.

6. Pick a fight with them, then they'll ground you to your room and be so mad at you they'll forget you have any homework. This is one of my favorites.

7. Beat up your little brother and you'll be grounded to your room again, and they'll forget to ask you about it.

8. Hide in the bathroom and take a shower for as long as you can. Pretend you're brushing your teeth *and* flossing. Cut your toenails. Keep stalling.

9. Go to bed early and hide under the covers listening to the ball game on your Sony Walkman. Parents think it's cool when you go to bed early.

10. This is the best one of all, do the dinner dishes and they'll be so shocked and pleased they won't dare mention homework the rest of the night.

Thank you, Strangelove Malone.

Can you believe this calculating little sucker? At first I thought he was exaggerating, but as we discussed his strategies in more detail, I began to realize they were all true! He'd used every single one of them on at least one occasion.

See what you're up against?

These kid techniques have one thing in common; they take advantage of contemporary family life. As a parent, you only have so much energy left at the end of the day—there are meals to prepare, errands to run, car pools, sport activities, church/temple activities, a constant stream of demands on your time and attention.

The homework-avoiding ADHD kid uses these situations to his advantage every chance he gets. To combat the problem, you need to start being more pro-active rather than re-active, and learn how to keep one step ahead.

For example, what do you do if your kid keeps "forgetting" to bring his books from school?

One solution is to keep another set of books at home. Sure, this may cost you an extra few bucks, but it's a sound investment that will save you countless hours in fruitless arguing.

Or what if you hear, "I did my homework in studyhall," or "I don't have any." A couple of phone calls to school will take care of this one. Our fourteen-year-old daughter's school has a Homework Hotline, whereby all homework for that day is spelled out on an answering machine. She hates it!

Even a simple assignment notebook ought to close the gap, with both you and the teachers communicating about homework on a daily basis. The more involved you are in what your kid is doing in school, the less chance he has of taking advantage of your busyness/ignorance/denial.

Aside from taking advantage of busyness, Strangelove Malone and Company also go out of their way to increase chaos within the home, a natural skill many ADHD kids are born with—knowing how to up the ante which diverts attention from the real issues.

Having an ADHD kid in your home suggests you already spend much of your time in a chaotic environment, so all he has to do is crank up the heat a little, and there's another full-scale crisis blowing, making homework less of a priority.

What steps can you take to decrease the chaos?

Environment

When:

The first line of defense in reducing chaos is to call upon our old friend, structure. Establishing a set homework schedule is a must. This means working out an agreement with your kid that he'll start doing his homework at the same time each night for an agreed-upon time period.

Where:

We parents tend to think homework should be done in a quiet room, sitting at a desk or table with no music or other stimuli. And while that would appear to make sense, it might not be the best setting for your average ADHD kid. In fact, these may be the very conditions that spark a major rebellion because they're too restrictive and confining. Consequently, his first instinct is to get away as fast as possible, heralding the onset of a new battle.

Strange as it may sound, some kids *do* study much better with background noise—music, for example, or with some other artificially produced sound.

I know of a couple of computer geek ADHD teenagers who make their own "sound machines," using computers and stereo systems. These sound machines are electronic devices that produce "white noise," a form of static that sounds like ocean surf or a moaning wind. (Incidentally, these are two supposedly not-so-smart kids!)

Other kids study well with music. I realize that when you hear some of the godawful sounds your son or daughter's CD player produces, there's no way you and I would call it music, but *they* do, and it helps them concentrate.

When you were sixteen what did you call music? "Louie, Louie?" "I Rode Through the Desert on a Horse with No Name?" "Me and You and a Dog Named Boo?" "War Pigs," by Black Sabbath? Or perhaps you were more of a Neil Sedaka or Carpenters type, you poor thing . . .

But for Junior, here, his music helps him focus.

Of course, you need to make sure that this really is the case. If you allow your kid to study with music or with the TV on, but you notice his grades become even worse, then it's not working; he's showing you that he needs to study in a quieter environment. Likewise, if your kid tries to study with the music cranked up to 2,000 decibels, you might suggest that it's a teensy-weensy bit too loud!

How:

As I write this, I'm lying sprawled on the floor of my office. Although my colleagues are used to me by now, some of their clients who walk past my open door (I don't want to miss anything) often raise an eyebrow, but hey, it works for me; sitting at a desk doesn't.

Be flexible. Allow your kid to experiment. Let him discover what works best for him. The novelty of lying on the floor, hanging upside down off the edge of his bed, or another weird study position may very well allow him to harness that elusive concentration.

Speaking of which, the best example of weird study habits comes from a guy I was at college with in Scotland, a guy who shall remain nameless. At exam time, Nameless would light foul-smelling incense sticks, tape all his notes to the ceiling, lie on his back on the floor, and read his notes through binoculars while listening to Deep Purple records.

Why:

When any of us asked Nameless about his bizarre study habits, he claimed the binoculars allowed him to read only one line at a time, as well as giving him something to do with his hands. He'd also study wearing nothing but his underwear and black socks.

As far as I know, Nameless didn't use drugs. The only explanation he ever gave for his bizarre behavior was always the same— "It helps me concentrate."

Obviously, he needed several of his senses stimulated at the same time—sight, hearing, smell, and touch. That was just the way he was, and by accepting himself, he found out what worked best for him. Nowadays we would call Nameless a *Multi-Sensory Learner*. Back then, we simply called him a geek. The place in which he studied would be called a *Multi-Sensory Environment*, (although he referred to it as The Pit), a technique used with ADHD and LD kids in the more innovative schools. I guess Nameless was ahead of the times without any of us realizing it.

Experiment with Multi-Sensory environments for your kid, and find out what really does work best for him or her.

For those of you who wish to take this to extremes, provide popcorn, Ding-Dongs, and soft drinks for your kid. If as a result, his study habits improve, he's what we call an *Intake Learner!* I'm serious, that's what it's called! Remember, this is America, we have a label for *everything!*

Time Management

The thought of sitting down for an hour straight makes most ADHD kids break out in hives, generally freaks them out, and makes them feel like the Prisoner of Zenda.

One effective way around this is to use the "Baby steps" method of studying—study for thirteen minutes, two-minute break, thirteen and two, and so on.

Breaking up time in this manner reduces the experience of feeling overwhelmed, that familiar "I-don't-know-where-to-begin" response, a common cause of so many academic problems.

The thirteen and two-minute system makes time perception much more manageable to the ADHD mind. These reduced time segments allow your kid to see task completion more frequently, providing him with instant feedback, which in turn enhances his motivation to keep going.

ADHD kids thrive on regular, positive feedback, mainly because they're so lousy at giving it to themselves, a side effect from all those years of hearing what screw-ups they are.

If ADHD kids don't receive positive feedback, even though they see they're doing a good job, they usually just quit half way through. Then you yell at them. Then they refuse to try again. Then . . . well, you know how this one goes.

One-On-One Help

Having such strong needs for feedback, ADHD kids often flourish with one-on-one attention in homework situations. This doesn't mean doing the work for them, but it does mean acting as a guide/coach/cheerleader. Being present as they complete tasks helps anchor them, and clears up any confusion they may have about the material. Throwing in a couple of encouraging words at the same time does wonders for a flagging spirit.

On the other hand, not having one-on-one support allows attentional breakdown, and permits wandering minds to wander away completely, an experience all too familiar to me.

In boarding school we were expected to do homework every night for two hours en masse in a giant, cavernous studyhall. Supervision consisted of eight prefects sitting at raised desks on the perimeter of the studyhall from where they looked down upon a sea of restless adolescents. These prefects were staff-appointed monitors, Responsible Students as far as the school administration was concerned. The good news was that if I didn't attract too much attention, I could usually just sit there and do my own thing. The bad news was that being able to do my own thing allowed my attention to take an extended vacation.

My typical study schedule between 5:00 P.M. and 7:00 P.M. went as follows:

5:00 - 5:15 Read the latest *MAD* magazine

5:15 - 5:30 Complete a crossword puzzle. I had
a book full of them.

5:30 - 5:35 Try to catch another student's attention. This never worked because Heid the Ball, my closest neighbor was usually asleep by this time.

5:35 - 5:45 Study Incan methods of human sacrifice.

5:45 - 5:50 Try to make a pinhole camera out of
a matchbox and light-sensitive paper. Take
picture of Heid the Ball drooling on his
book.

5:50 - 6:00 Nap, one hand holding my head and the
other holding a pen so that I appear to be
studying. Have to dry out book page due
to me drooling all over it.

6:01 - 6:01 Open my math book, but pass out from
fright at seeing algebraic equations.

6:02 - 6:10 Tap out tunes from the Top Twenty with my
pen.

6:10 - 6:15 Look at my English homework. Poetry.
"Dulce Et Decorum Est," by Wilfred Owen,

a poem about the stupidity of war. I write a short essay on why not only is war stupid, but any kind of militant coercion or domination. The following day the school administration views my essay as insubordination. Receive an "F"

6:16 - 6:21 Ask myself why I don't leave this school. My usual answer is that it must be God's will to punish me for being a Producer of Unadulterated Rubbish.

6:22 - 6:30 Feign a heart attack, clutching my chest and falling sideways out of my chair.

6:34 - 6:40 Eat carbon paper so that my lips turn blue to back up my claim of a heart attack.

6:43 - 6:44 Decide to sit up again because no one notices my medical emergency. Prefect gives me a demerit for creating a disturbance, and for wearing dark blue lipstick.

6:45 - 6:50 Attempt a Latin translation, but once again, start making up my own stories. Receive a "B" for entertaining my teacher. (The next day I translate the entire passage correctly to reward his belief in me.)

6:52 - 6:55 Think about naked women but have to stop when I suddenly remember this is a sin.

6:56 - 7:00 Try to figure out how earthworms eat to take my mind off naked women. I'd seen one earlier today (an earthworm, not a naked woman) and couldn't find its mouth.

7:04 P.M. Receive another demerit, this time for being late for Evening Prayer due to me losing track of time while trying to find out about worm mouths.

And you think you have a hard time living with an ADHD kid? Try living *as* an ADHD kid!

There's no question, a little one-on-one help can go a long way. Although I would have resisted the idea of close supervision when studying, I suspect there might have been an improvement in my grades if I'd had more one-on-one supervision. Or am I just kidding myself?

Incidentally, if any of you do know how earthworms eat, drop me a line because I never did get around to finding out the answer.

Motivation

First of all, let's take a look at some techniques that *don't* accomplish anything in the motivation department:

Nagging:

If your kid has reduced you to nagging about his non-compliance regarding homework, you probably nag on automatic pilot, unaware that you're even nagging. Ask yourself, be honest, does it really work?

Of course not! You're dealing with ADHD, a condition in which tuning you out is second nature, maybe even first nature.

Don't believe me? Try it and see. Make a tape recording of yourself using these famous nagging phrases:

Don't you ever listen?
Take out the trash!
Where's your book bag?
How many times do I have to tell you?
If I've told you once, I've told you a thousand times!
Because I'm your mother, that's why!
You can't go out looking like that!
Don't argue!
Wait till your father gets home!
Do as I say, not as I do!
You expect me to believe that?
I'm not someone else's mother!
Don't you look at me like that!
You want me to wipe that smile off your face?
Don't you use that tone of voice with me!
Who do you think you're talking to?
What kind of a report card do you call this?
What do you mean, you got another detention?
Where's your homework?
Do your homework!
Where's your assignment notebook?
Did you take your Ritalin?
Did you take a shower?
Did you brush your teeth?
You expect that dog to feed himself?
Where's your house key?
Turn that stereo down!
Turn out those lights!
You think money grows on trees?
Quit picking your nose!
Say "Excuse me."
What do you mean, the dog ate your homework?

Okay, now play the tape back and listen. Sounds pretty awful, huh? And this is supposed to improve motivation? Sorry folks, nagging doesn't work.

Grounding:

Or what about using grounding as a way to motivate? Not a chance! We know for a fact this doesn't work because if you say, "You're grounded!" he'll say, "I don't care!" and he still won't do his homework, as in the case of Matt, a fifteen-year-old boy with ADHD HIT.

Whenever Matt wouldn't do his homework, his parents grounded him for weeks at a time. As a result, not only did he refuse do his homework, he went berserk at being grounded for so long. He'd barricade himself in his room, jump out the window, and run away from home.

During our last counseling session, I asked Matt what he thought would motivate him. His reply was "Not grounding me for a million years. If it was only for a couple of days, I think I could handle it."

My initial internal reaction was "Yeah, right!" but I wanted to give him the benefit of the doubt. It turned out that in Matt's time-distorted mind, the thought of a two or three-week grounding made him feel as if he were receiving a life sentence. Matt convinced us that a shorter time frame was much more manageable, and would generate a less maniacal response. Finally, a situation in which grounding would be effective!

Bolstered by our "breakthrough," his beleaguered parents tried grounding him for only two days when he refused to do his homework. But Matt's response was, "I don't care! I still ain't doin' it!"

You win some, you lose some. Now we were back to square one. Like I mentioned earlier, grounding doesn't always work too well.

Other Things that don't Work too well

- Locking him in a closet (illegal)
- Sending him to military school (he'll get himself kicked out)
- Ignoring him (good luck)
- Pawning him off to Aunt Matilda in Alaska
- Sprinkling powdered Ritalin on his food (illegal)
- Pleading and begging
- Asking him to be "nice" and do his homework
- Signing him up as a foreign exchange student
- Sending him to a monastery (didn't work with me)

Effective Motivation (Stuff that does Work)

About half an hour ago in my office (by this time I was off the floor and in a chair) I met with a twelve-year-old boy, Josh, who was having problems with homework, meaning he refused to do any.

His main complaint was that his parents gave him too much help. They interfered so often, he simply refused to attempt any assignments in protest. That was his excuse anyway.

As he and I talked, his eyes suddenly filled with tears, catching me off guard. When I asked him why he was so upset, he related the following:

"My mom is always snooping in my book bag. She won't give me any privacy and makes me feel like a little kid."

"That's because you keep hiding your assignments and progress reports," I replied. "If you showed her your work voluntarily, she wouldn't need to rummage through your stuff. You've taught her not to trust you."

He gave me a quizzical look. Actually, it was more of a look that said he thought I was nuts. So he said, "Are you nuts? You're telling me *I* made this happen?"

"Sure. Cause and effect. You don't do your assignments; she searches your book bag. It's that simple. Show her your assignments, she'll back off."

"But if I show them to her, that'll mean I have to do them! No way!"

"Way. The only chance you have of getting any privacy and respect is by doing your homework."

Unconvinced, Josh argued with me for about ten minutes until a faint smile appeared on his face. "That means I wouldn't be doing homework just to keep her happy but because it would give me privacy? She won't ever need to go in my book bag again. Cool!"

"Duh!" I said in my best professional counselor's voice. "Your motivator, the reason for you to start doing homework is that it'll get the old parental units off your back and out of your stuff."

Then I saw a crease of suspicion furrow his brow, like he was having second thoughts. "You'd better not be conning me," he said.

I smiled. "Who, me?"

"Okay," he said, left my office, and went out to tell his skeptical parents in the waiting room.

After Josh left, the next kid I met with was Tim who was bemoaning the fact that when he tried to do his homework, Mom and Dad hovered over him like two hungry hawks circling a field mouse. Please note this was his analogy, not mine. Not too shabby for a kid who's flunking English.

I sat across from him. "Hovering over you? That's because if they leave you alone you won't do it."

"Yeah, I know, but they make me feel like a total dork, so I get mad and quit doing it." He mimicked Mom, "Now, Tim, if I have four apples and you take away two, how many do I have left?" He shook his head in disgust. "Apples suck! I hate apples. She's *obsessed* with apples! She always talks to me like I'm a dorky third grader!"

"Maybe she does that because you act like you're a dorky third grader, pretending you don't know what's expected of you."

I thought he was going to leap out the chair and come after me, but instead, he pouted, refusing to speak.

I decided to try a different tack. Time to implement the Win-Win technique. "Look, Tim, why did your parents bring you to see me?"

He rolled his eyes, and finally looked over at me. "'Cause I got ADHD. Okay!"

"Wrong! They brought you here so I could teach you how to train them properly. Although, they don't know that."

"Huh?"

"Sure. They don't know how to treat you like the mature thirteen-year-old you are. They treat you like you're a geek; they don't respect you or anything. We have to train them."

Now I had his interest. "Like, how, dude?"

"Training a parent is simple. In fact, parents are easier to train than dogs once you get the hang of it. Okay, name something you want them to change."

"I already told you I want them to quit talking to me like I'm a dumb eight-year-old."

"When do they do that the most?"

"Any time I don't do my homework."

"Aha! So if you *do* your homework, and they still talk to you like you're an eight-year-old, then they're gonna look real stupid, aren't they, ha ha."

Tim thought about this for several seconds, then a look came over his face that I can only describe as devilish glee. "Yeah! And if they go through my stuff looking for hidden progress reports and don't find any, they'll feel like total dorks!"

Fast-thinking Tim was on a roll, "And I bet it'd work with teachers, too. Hey, dude! You can really kick butt when you learn how to train the adults in your life!"

Excited by the prospect of kicking adult butt all over town, Tim started doing homework, astonishing everyone.

The outcome of his adult butt-kicking campaign was that his parents and skeptical teachers were thrilled, not to mention that Tim's self-esteem began to improve for two reasons:

1) he gradually improved his grades

2) he went from thinking of himself as a sullen
   loser to becoming a winner, Master of the Adult
   Butt-kicking Universe

So often we say a kid has no motivation, but that's not strictly true. With both Josh and Tim, their motivation needed to be *re-directed*. They had motivation, but it wasn't being channeled or managed. Now they had a reason for putting up with the drudgery of homework and classwork—it was the pathway to training adults.

An additional benefit was that not only did their grades and attitudes improve, but they also found their parents eventually began to give them more trust and freedom, prized possessions in the teenage world.

Any time they were tempted to resort to their old home-work-avoiding behavior, they reminded themselves that if they slipped backwards, they'd be letting their parents win, a fate worse than death!

Obviously, this is the simplified, shortened version; the transformation didn't happen overnight. But with consistent counseling and coaching, both kids became more successful by having their motivation re-directed and harnessed.

So what motivates *your* kid? What is the fire you can light underneath him to bring about success?

You know the old saying about "You can lead a horse to water, but you can't make it drink?" (Or in the case of college kids, "You can lead a girl to Vasser, but you can't make her think.") Same thing applies to motivation. You can't force a kid to be motivated because ultimately that has to come from within. But you can *re-frame* and harness motivation with the right carrots and sticks.

All of us have different motivators, and your child is no exception. Take a moment and think about what motivates your kid:

Money:

In our materialistic society, it shouldn't come as any big surprise that a certain number of kids are motivated by money.

Does that mean you need to bribe your kid into doing homework? Hopefully not, but perhaps a couple of greenbacks floating around on the horizon might just be the carrot and stick he needs. For example, "If you keep your grades at least "B"s or even "C"s for the entire quarter, you can have a new videogame."

Don't go haywire; he doesn't need a new $1,000 stereo or a new car, for crying out loud! Let's be realistic, here.

So is this bribery or motivation? I don't know. Try it and see. If it works, it's motivation. If it doesn't, it's a pathetic attempt at bribery. You decide.

Power:

The thought of having "power over parents" was what motivated Tim and Josh. The idea of being able to train adults and make them look dumb if they didn't recognize accomplishment was an effective motivator. Use the "reverse psychology" concepts of Win-Win to harness and re-frame your kid's motivation.

Freedom:

Many kids complain about not having enough freedom. Use this hunger to increase motivation. For example, "If you do the following with regard to homework, then we'll *fill in the blank* for you. The blank should offer an increase of freedom and independence:

1. Allow him to experiment with study environments. By making these his choices instead of you imposing yours, you may see more progress.

2. Allow him to complete homework assignments without parental interference, based on the premise that if he follows through and *does it properly*, you'll get off his back.

3. Allow him to stay up ten minutes later on the weekend if he does complete assignments, or extend weekend curfew by ten minutes.

4. Come up with your own versions of increased freedom.

Praise:

Otherwise known as "positive reinforcement." Have you any idea how many negative messages your child hears about himself on any given day—"You're wrong," "You blew it again," "You screwed up," "No, not that way, *this* way, dummy!" "Pay attention, bird brain!" and so on.

Are you really surprised that he has problems with self-esteem?

Any time you feed these negative messages to a kid, they multiply in his mind like a virus, eating away at his sense of self.

If you've heard the message, "You're a loser" either ver-
bally or even non-verbally with eye rolls and exaggerated
sighs, several times a day from about age six to fifteen, that's
nine year's worth of hearing "You're a loser," about 10,000
times!

But don't despair! One of the amazing facets of the human mind is the ability to forget all this garbage, and undo the
damage.

Do you remember the "Saturday Night Live" character
of Stuart Smalley, created and played by Al Franken in the
late 80's?

Stuart was a parody of the 12-Step recovery movement—Adult Children of Alcoholics, Overeaters Anonymous,
and all the other 12-Step programs. Stuart's catchphrase was
"I'm good enough, I'm smart enough, and doggone it, people
like me!" Stuart was into self-affirmation in a big way.

And while this was all very funny, the fact remains that
Stuart was right—these kinds of positive affirmations can
erase years of damage to a kid's self-esteem.

The negative messages are stored on the neurological
equivalent of a cassette tape. Hearing frequent positive messages is like taping over a bad tape, replacing the negative
with positive.

But don't get carried away. If Ryan brings home a "D"
instead of an "F", or even completes an entire assignment,
don't bombard him with ridiculous attaboys like "How mar-
velous!" "You're such a genius!" "Harvard Medical School
here we come!" "Congratulations! Here's a new BMW!"

Not only will Ryan think you're being sarcastic and in-
sincere, he'll think you're more weird than he already thought
you were, and won't take your praise seriously. A gradual
increase will give you more credibility.

Fear:

In the short-term, fear may *seem* to work as a motivator, but in the big picture, any motivating effects quickly wear off. All you'll have done is drive your kid further underground and make him sneakier.

Don't get me wrong, healthy fear, based in reality, has its place—"If you don't complete your studies, you won't graduate, you won't have a career, and you won't have any money because we're going to spend all your inheritance before we die, you lazy slob."

As a tool to demonstrate the reality of cause and effect, fear is useful, but as a long-term motivator, forget it!

Tutors

Another useful strategy to aid you in winning the Homework Wars is to enlist the aid of a tutor. Hiring a tutor can be a sound investment, assuming the one you hire has a thorough understanding and experience in working with ADHD kids.

The advantages of hiring a tutor include:

1. Tutors provide the one-on-one structure and guidance your kid needs to successfully complete assignments.

2. As non-family members, tutors tend to be excluded from traditional family power struggles.

3. Tutors won't automatically put your kid in a scapegoat role as they're typically from outside the family and school environments.

4. The novelty of a new person often enhances motivation.

5. Observing a tutor experienced in working with ADHD kids can teach you new ways to deal with your kid.

6. They give you a much-needed break.

A disadvantage is that regular tutoring can be expensive. Sometimes schools provide free or minimal-cost tutoring services. Or perhaps you can recruit a teacher friend. Contact your school district, your local chapter of the Learning Disabilities Association, or CH.A.D.D. to find out if there are any tutors in your neighborhood.

Please note: If you do decide to go this route, and your kid is a teenage boy, I'd suggest not hiring a pretty, eighteen-year-old female tutor. She might be a wee bit of a distraction.

In conclusion, we find that the best techniques for winning the Homework Wars are:

- Routine and structure
- Effective environment
- Schedule which permits regular breaks
- One-on-one attention

- Discovering and using motivators
- No nagging
- Using tutors (no pretty eighteen-year-olds)

Chapter 13

ADHD and Social Skills:
Quit Picking Your Nose!

Travis is an ADHD kid who recently started counseling to help him improve his social skills.

Prior to our first session, his mom called from her car phone to say she was supposed to meet Travis at the office but was currently stuck in traffic. She asked if I would go ahead and start Travis's session without her.

"Fine," I said. Travis was seventeen, so I was sure there'd be no problems, naï ve fool that I was!

Arriving for his session twenty minutes late, Travis crashed through the door of the waiting room, grabbed the intake paperwork from Jasmine, our secretary, and flopped down onto one of the couches. Nothing unusual about that except he almost sat on top of a nervous woman waiting to see one of my colleagues.

With a rapidly escalating sense of dread, I watched his performance through a crack in the frosted-glass window that separates the waiting room from the counseling suites.

He proceeded to read every question aloud from the intake form, glancing up expectantly at the startled woman as if she would know the answers. Not receiving any response from her, Travis gave up, and hurriedly scribbled down his own answers, muttering under his breath.

When he finished, he sat the clipboard on his lap, and started tapping it against his thigh, humming the theme to the movie, *Jaws.* He smiled over at the woman and said, "Sharks. I'm into sharks." He cleared his throat loudly. Then he picked his nose, grossing out the woman who had now scurried over to a seat in the corner, cowering behind a copy of *People* magazine.

But the show wasn't over yet, oh no; Travis was merely warming up. The waiting room door opened again and a family of four entered.

"Hi!" Travis yelled. "How're y'all doing?" he asked in a 200-decibel voice, startling the family half to death.

The last straw was when I heard him belching none too delicately. I rushed into the waiting room to rescue everyone. "Hi, Travis," I said, and steered him down the short hallway to my office.

He stopped walking and faced me. "Do you like sharks?" he asked, then not waiting for a reply, lumbered on into the office. He wandered around, and picked up various items from my desk. He examined them for a moment, muttered quietly to himself, then moved on to the next one.

Travis finally sat down—in *my* chair, I might add.

"Your mom called to say she was running late. She'll be here soon," I said.

"You're a lot shorter than I thought you'd be. You talk kinda funny, too," Travis said, laughing through his nose like a wildebeest at a feeding trough.

"Travis, why do you think you're mom wanted you to meet with me?" I asked.

He spun his head around toward my desk. "Hey, got any games on that computer? *Doom? Cyber Death Nazis Nuke a Cute Purple Dinosaur?*"

"Your mom. Why does she want you to see me?"

"Oh, she says I've got problems with social skills, whatever that is," he said, leaping up out of his chair. He marched over to the computer, and played around on the keyboard trying to figure out the password.

Yep, Travis had jumped right in there with his social skills. I had a feeling this was going to be a long session.

Obviously, Travis is one of the more extreme examples of an ADHD kid with poor social skills.

On the other extreme is sixteen-year-old Jennifer. When I handed her the intake paperwork (Jasmine was too busy doing her nails at this point), she appeared startled. Quickly composing herself, she smiled sheepishly, and handed the clipboard to her mother, who, in turn, handed it right back to her.

When I went back out to the waiting room ten minutes later, Jennifer still hadn't completed the forms.

I called her name and she jumped as if suddenly awakened from a deep sleep. "What?" she said. "Oh, the papers. Sorry, guess I was daydreaming."

Mom glared at her. "So what else is new?" Mom said, looking up at me. "I told her she'd better hurry up and fill out the forms but she just ignored me, and *I* certainly wasn't going to do them for her. That's her responsibility, not mine."

I guess Mom was on her last nerve.

Jennifer doesn't have too many friends. Some of the other girls at school laugh at her, and call her names like "Clueless" and "Airhead."

She spent most of the session nodding her head, and making "Mm . . ." sounds, not listening to much of what I said. When she did speak, she paused as if searching for the right word, then she'd look up at me and ask, "What was the question again?"

I sat on the edge of my chair, and leaned toward her, hoping my increased proximity would get her attention.

"Jennifer, are you bored?"

She shrugged. "I'm sorry. I guess I must be."

"Me, too," I said softly. That sure got her attention!

"Excuse me? Are you calling me boring?" she asked, her eyes wide with surprise.

"Nah, just kidding. Had to get your attention somehow. Anyway, we were talking about how the other girls seem to ignore you . . ."

Even though Travis and Jennifer are at opposite ends of the introvert/extrovert scale, the outcome is the same—poor social skills.

Below, I've outlined the symptoms that cause the most social difficulty for ADHD kids, dividing them ADHD HIT (Hyperactive-Impulsive Types) and ADHD PIT (Predominantly Inattentive Types).

HIT Reasons for Poor Social Skills

- Interrupts
- Constant frustration
- Domineering
- Doesn't respect physical space of others
- Laughs inappropriately
- Insults others (inadvertently)
- Talks too much
- Rambles
- Talks too fast and/or too loud
- Inconsistent eye contact

- Impatient
- Misses verbal and non-verbal cues
- High distractibility

You can see why these behaviors would cause poor social skills, no matter what age your kid is.

Naturally, other kids have difficulty being friends with HIT kids because of their dominance and tornadic demeanor, especially at play.

HIT Social Skills and Play

In classroom settings, your HIT child probably does better in one-on-one situations than in groups. Same thing applies to social functioning. Your average ADHD kid usually does fine socially one-on-one, unless the other kid also has ADHD HIT, in which case you've just poured a bucketload of gasoline onto a smoldering fire.

Let's say your kid and one of his friends are getting along, playing happily. Then a third kid joins them—the smoldering fire glowing just below the surface is about to become an inferno! That's because your HIT kid can *almost* handle one other kid without incident, but a third is overwhelming, making too many demands on his attention.

But don't despair; there is a way your ADHD HIT kid can prevent an explosion—he can insist his friends play only by *his* rules, which are as follows:

1. If I'm losing the game, we stop playing.

2. We only do what I say when I say it.

3. If I say you're out the game, then you are.

4. You must accept me as Supreme Commander of the Entire Universe (SCEU).

As far as he's concerned, this solution is quite simple and logical. The fact that his two friends will resent his unfairness, and maybe even quit playing with him doesn't enter his little head.

But even if his friends decide to go along with these rules, eventually someone will get thwocked on the head, thrown into the mud, or have his GI Joe set on fire accompanied by a gleeful 1,000-decibel voice yelling, "I'm melting! I'm melting!"

And so is the solarian kitchen floor because your kid is now melting GI Joes in the kitchen because it's raining outside. When you start yelling about this minor detail, your ADHD HIT kid explains, "We had to bring the GI Joes inside or the rain would put the flames out and I'm really pleased with myself for using the common sense you're always telling me I don't have but I don't know why you're having such a cow because I finally thought something through before making a decision just like you're always telling me to do!"

And did you know that if you drop a flaming GI Joe from a great height, like his sister's second floor bedroom, or even from the roof, when it hits the ground it makes a really cool "splat!" sound? See, if only you would understand these things, you wouldn't be so upset all the time.

But you are upset, and his friends are upset that you're yelling at all of them, especially Little Frankie, who got hit on the head with a screwdriver by your kid.

Tearfully, Frankie explains this is all because *he* won the stupid game, and your dumb kid got mad, and he's never going to play with your stupid, dorky kid again, and no wonder all the other kids hate your kid!

One reason there is so much turmoil around the playing of games is that the ADHD HIT kid misses so many necessary social cues, like why did the other two kids suddenly start yelling at him and run home just because he tapped Little Frankie lightly on the head with a screwdriver for winning the game? Don't they know that as SCEU (Supreme Commander of the Entire Universe), only he can win?

Non-ADHD kids tend to view HIT kids as domineering, selfish, short-tempered, unfair in how they play, and in how they socialize. What the other kids (and their parents) may not realize is that so often the ADHD kid's domineering behavior stems from "trying too hard," a futile attempt at covering up feelings of low self-esteem, inadequacy, and frustration.

The HIT kid believes from bitter experience that he will soon be rejected. He knows he does something wrong but has no clue as to what. Feeling uptight and defensive, he jumps right into his familiar scapegoat role, creating a self-fulfilling prophecy of peer rejection. Then he feels hurt, confused, and angry, wondering yet again, why the other kids don't want to play with him.

HIT Social Skills Solutions

As ADHD kids are such poor self-observers with a tendency to blame everyone else for their problems, giving them regular feedback on their social skills is necessary:

- Ask questions: If your kid is upset after a social faux pas, ask direct questions about the situation like "What happened?" "How did you act?" "What did you say?" "What did they say?" "Did you hit anyone on the head with a mallet?" Break down his interactions and show him where you think he went wrong.

- Cause and Effect: Teach him there's a direct relationship between him calling his friends "Poopheads," clobbering them, and so on, and the fact that they don't want to play with him any more. Teach him that when he acts *this* way, that happens, when he acts *that* way, this happens.

- "Fake it till you make it." This is an old AA slogan that means even though you're still struggling to learn a new behavior, if you act as if you've *already* learned that behavior, you'll learn it more quickly.

- Role Reversal: You pretend to be him, and he pretends to be one of his friends. Act out a scenario in which you yell at him or have a tantrum because you're not getting your way. Let him see what he's like when he acts out. Afterwards, ask how he felt when you yelled at him, as a way of showing how his friends must feel when he yells at them.

- Technology: If you're really sneaky and have the opportunity, videotape him and his friends, then

play the tape back to him, pointing out the interactions which are problem areas. If you don't have
access to video, use a cassette recorder. Let him
hear how demanding and rude he is! Be direct but
tactful when you point out the problems.

Make use of all these opportunities to show him how he
can improve. He can't figure any of this out by himself, that's
why he needs your help.

And if he complains about you being sneaky because you
used videotape, tell him I told you to, that it's all my fault,
and he can write me to complain!

PIT Reasons for Poor Social Skills

Now we take a look at the social problems common to
PIT kids. Sharing the same base of low self-esteem as the
Hyper Harrys, PIT kids know they're "different," but their
social problems show up quite differently from the HIT kids'.

The PIT is the one whom the other kids never call, never
pick first to play games, are treated as if they're invisible,
and/or are bullied by more dominant kids.

PIT reasons for poor social skills include:

- Doesn't initiate
- Daydreams
- Doesn't pay attention
- Doesn't listen

- Appears aloof
- Inconsistent or no eye contact
- Understimulated
- Too much internal "static"
- Thinks about a million things at the same time
- Misses verbal cues
- Misses non-verbal cues
- Easily distracted
- Invisible
- Victimized

A special word about that last one, victimized. Because they're so unaware of what's going on around them and have tendencies toward shyness, some PIT kids are bullied and picked on. They're not sure why that happens and eventually conclude this is just the way life is, that there's no way out.

Having few friends, they often find themselves alone in school settings, and in doing so, set themselves up as targets for bullies. Even if the PIT kids understand there is safety in numbers, they still don't know how to connect with a group.

Major problems arise if we let them continue in their "difference" without intervention. They slip into a chronic, quiet despair by the time they reach adolescence, feeling rejected, lonely, and worthless. If the pattern continues, they often become depressed, withdrawn, and inwardly hostile, silently angry toward their peers whom they see as being more socially successful.

When they're bullied, they don't know how to respond. They put up with it more and more until one day, they simply freak out and end up taking a baseball bat to the bully. They now find themselves in even more trouble, which pushes them further into a cycle of believing they're worthless screw-ups who now have violence added to their rap sheets of mistakes.

Due to their constant daydreaming and "zoning out" they miss the subtle social cues required for effective communication and successful social relationships.

They even miss the punchlines to jokes, causing the other kids to think "Man, what a geek!" or "What's his deal?" spiraling them further into the vicious cycle of alienation and ostracization.

PIT Social Skills and Play

At play, the PIT may become bored out of his skull within thirty seconds of playing a game. To make matters worse, if it's a new game, he probably wasn't paying enough attention to learn how it's played, and now doesn't want to look like a total geek by asking for the rules to be repeated.

His solution? Make up the rules as he goes along until:

- He quits
- Argues with the other two kids that they don't know how to play
- Starts picking his nose and flicks boogers at his two companions when they're not looking
- If he is ADHD CT (PIT with a few HIT streaks) he flicks boogers at them when they *are* looking.
- The other kids chase him away or beat him up.

These dynamics also apply to team sports, whereby your average ADHD kid (HIT, PIT, or CT) ends up getting mad early on in the game, feels frustrated and hurt, and just wants to bonk people on the head or run away.

As an ADHD CT kid myself with strong PIT tendencies, I always hated team sports, but in high school I didn't have much choice in the matter. Living in Scotland where the primary religion is soccer, I had to play three times a week. I still have Post Traumatic Flashbacks any time I see a soccer ball.

I just didn't get it. You were supposed to chase a ball around a field (a rain-filled mud pit) but you're not allowed to touch the damn thing with your hands; you had to use your feet. Then when you finally kicked the ball into a net, (hopefully the other team's) all the other kids would start hugging and grab each other! I still don't get it.

Maybe the fact that I have the athletic ability of a potted plant had something to do with my aversion to soccer. Being able to make my right foot follow my left without tripping was always a major feat.

There were just too many details. The thought of having to do the following was overwhelming—run after a ball and kick it into a net (I didn't realize it made a difference which net you kicked it into), keep an eye on a bunch of wild maniacs yelling at you to give *them* the ball (some of whom were on the other side, but of course, I couldn't tell which was which), avoid a 250-pound gorilla-child whose mission it was to maim you for life, then figure out you could only kick the ball within certain lines and boundaries which were never drawn or marked, so how were you supposed to know where the damn lines were in the first place! And finally, make sure your own team didn't kill you for kicking the ball into your own net!

What a fuss they made about a game! In later life, I learned soccer was supposed to be fun, as opposed to being weird, what with all the butt-grabbing and hugging when they scored a goal, not to mention lynching me from the goal post after we lost 54-6, because twenty-four of the other side's goals came from my confusion about which goal-net was which. Details, details . . .

Naturally, when choosing sides, I was always last to be picked. The other kids would hear "Okay, you can be Center Forward," or "You're Full-Back." I'd hear, "Oh, no, he's still hanging around! Okay, Quinn, you can be Left Behind, ha ha!" or "You can be the goal post, ha ha!"

But the laugh was on them because I learned some things as a goal post, like if you're standing there in the mud trying to figure out how earth worms eat, you can sustain painful injuries to your face when a soccer ball smashes into it at 200 mph!

The following semester, I decided I'd better try to learn how to do the soccer thing—my life depended on it.

The only problem was that my dad didn't watch or play soccer, and although he did his best to teach me what he did know (almost nothing) there was a certain lack of enthusiasm in his instruction. He was far more interested in math and electronics, along with an obsession with growing tomatoes in his greenhouse.

I knew he was embarrassed at how pitiful a soccer player I was, so I decided to earn his respect another way. He'd been complaining that there were too many tomatoes in the greenhouse, crowding out his other plants, a comment which gave me another of my "brilliant" ideas, an experiment which I just *knew* would make him very proud of me; I was going to combine two of his interests, namely the tomato plants and electronics to solve his plant crowding problem. I was going to blow up his largest tomato plants using electronics and a tablespoon of gunpowder I'd saved from a bunch of old fireworks.

With great anticipation, I connected several miles of copper wire to a couple of large batteries, then messed around with the ends of the wires until I generated some sparks. Seeing the little bright orange sparks flying around, I excitedly plunged the wires into the gunpowder-dusted tomatoes. . .

Have you any idea how much allowance money it takes to replace over thirty greenhouse windows?

Anyway, after the Great Exploding Tomato Experiment, dear old Dad doubled his efforts at teaching me how to play soccer:

Dad: "See this ball? Kick it!"
Me: "Kinda looks like a giant tomato, doesn't it?"
Dad: "On second thoughts, let's go fishing."

That was the end of my soccer education. From now on, I was on my own to figure out the intricacies and subtleties of team sports.

Eventually, I came up with a solution—I refused to play soccer again, ever. Of course, this sparked a riot in school because up until this point no one had ever refused to play before. Once again, I was back in my scapegoat role!

All was not lost, however. One of the priests, seeing me about to be lynched in the hallway, asked me if I wanted to go sailing with him.

"Sure beats the heck out of being lynched!" I said cheerfully, and hopped into his car, regaling him with tall tales of my previous seafaring adventures, all of which had taken place in the bathtub.

When we arrived at the harbor, he showed me the basics, and I jumped into the sailing boat with another anti-soccer geek. That day, we made Second Place in the Scottish High School Sailing Championship Race! Of course, I had no idea I was even in a competition, but I didn't care. All I cared about was the incredible feeling of freedom, leaning off the edge of the sailboat, skimming the white tops of the North Sea, yelling into the wind at the top of my lungs and not receiving any demerits for doing so!

Then I capsized the damn boat and my crewmember tried to beat me up as we bobbed around in the ice-cold swell of the North Sea. Still, it was better than playing soccer.

Bottom line is the old cliché, different strokes for different folks.

That particular teacher had stumbled on a solution for my lack of team social skills by channeling me into more individual sports or at least small group sports. What about your kid? What solutions are available to him?

PIT Social Skills Solutions

You help a PIT kid the same way you help an HIT kid, with bucketloads of feedback. Use whatever methods you have at your disposal, including the video, audio, your observations, anything that will shed light on what he's doing to alienate himself.

- Teach him how to stay attuned and not drift off by asking himself questions like "Am I drifting off?" "Am I paying attention?" "Am I bored?"

- Eye contact: Stress the importance of consistent eye contact. There are three reasons why his eye contact may not be up to par:

    a) the lower his self-esteem, the lower his eye contact

    b) breaking eye contact is a side-effect from daydreaming

    c) he may also suffer from Asperger's Syndrome, a condition which can resemble ADHD

Remember, some PIT kids have learned how to look as if they're making eye contact while zoning out as a way to keep nagging parents and teachers off their backs.

- Self-defense: If he's being bullied, teach him how to protect himself. First, you have to give him permission to defend himself, and secondly, you have to show him how. This might mean literally showing him how to fight. I know this is against the school rules but the reality is that if a kid is beating up your kid and your kid just stands there and takes it, he's just given the bully permission to keep nailing him. I know, I know, school policy states that any fighting will result in expulsion and so on, but in most cases we're not dealing with fighting, we're dealing with survival! Sign him up for karate or self-defense program. Very often, just knowing he can handle himself is transmitted to the other kids and they no longer mess with him, instead of him transmitting a victim message that he's fair game.

- Give him regular feedback about what you see him doing in social situations. Demonstrate and encourage him to use new approaches.

Observing teenagers is more difficult than with younger kids. It's not like you can say, "Yo, Skater Dude, me and Mom thought we might hang with you and the homeys," then you and the wife cruise on up to Dairy Queen in your baggy pants and reversed ball caps.

Are you crazy? Allow him to be seen with the old parental units? I thought we'd already established that was only to be used as a consequence! That and the Barry Manilow songs.

Nah, you have to be sneakier than that. Get feedback from brothers, sisters, teachers and counselors or anyone else who knows him well.

Remember the kid I mentioned at the beginning of this chapter, the nose-picking, space-invading, gas-passing, belching guy, Travis? Neither of his parents knew he engaged in half of these behaviors until I happened to observe him that time in the waiting room and told them.

TV Role Models and Social Skills

Teaching social skills is imperative for a civilized society as well as for a harmonious home. It's as if we think that politeness and courtesy are signs of weakness. But if we don't model these behaviors in our dealings with others, how can we expect our children to improve *their* social skills?

Where do your kids see social skills modeled on a frequent basis? Television, the Fount of Wisdom for generations.

We are supposed to be our kids' primary role models, but the reality is that so often our example is relegated to second place by the Loony Lantern, all 500 channels.

One of the problems in learning social skills from TV is that from a kid point of view, if it's on TV, then it must be true, this is The Way Things Are.

Who do your kids learn from?

"Bart Simpson?"
"Ren and Stimpy?"
"South Park?"
"Married with Children?"
"Melrose Place?"
"Days of our Lives?"
"Beavis and Butthead?"

The list is endless, people clambering over each other, insulting each other, displaying intolerance and prejudice, lying, stealing, killing, and belching.

But then, what's the alternative? Mr. Roger's Neighborhood? Why not? Fred is the epitome of politeness and tolerance.

Or what about that purple dinosaur, the one that looks like the results of a really bad acid trip, according to a young man I spoke with recently. He said, "If you make your kids watch Barney, they'll be really messed up when they go out into the real world! Me and my friends spend a lot of time coming up with ways to blow him up just because he bugs us so much!"

You want to know who influences your kid's social development, monitor his TV and put limits on the garbage he watches.

Social Development via Board Games

Appropriate social skills may be learned from playing board games. An effective way to model social skills is to play board games with your kid—show him how to win graciously, how to lose without having a tantrum, how to wait his turn, and how not to set the game on fire when he starts feeling bored.

I'm sure playing board games is one of your favorite pastimes, right up there with root canals, but it's usually worth the time and effort. Just pray he doesn't want to play Monopoly! Thankfully, the odds are he won't, because from an ADHD perspective, Monopoly is the worst game imaginable!

Actually, Monopoly is not a game; it's a torture device developed in 1933 by an unemployed, depressed engineer called Durrow, from Germantown, Pennsylvania, a guy who perhaps needed to get a life, badly.

Mr. Durrow's family were so concerned about how depressed and boring he'd become that in 1934, they persuaded him to approach Parker Brothers with his newly invented "game" so they wouldn't need to listen to him going on and on about how exciting it was.

Parker Brother executives test-played Monopoly, then rejected it completely on the grounds that it was slow-paced and had ridiculously complicated rules.

But due to an Act of God or a Twist of Fate, this torturous device finally made it to market, and Parker Brothers churned out a bunch of games, millions of them.

But hope was in sight because in December 1936, the company president, George Parker, decreed that the manufacturing plant quit production. That should have been the end, but you know how those Twists of Fate go.

Not knowing how to quell the potential riots from victims of the Great Depression (this was an economic thing as well as a side effect from playing Monopoly) the US Government had George start production up again so it could buy millions of games and issue them to every man, woman, and child in the country as a way to take their minds off poverty and hunger.

This generation then foisted Monopoly on succeeding generations every Christmas, in case there was ever another Depression. That along with stockpiles of canned Pork 'n' Beans.

You ever look inside the pantries of people who grew up in the Depression? Millions of canned goods, a couple of gold bars, and unopened games of Monopoly.

During the Wall St. Crash of 1987, I remember Old Man Nichols, my neighbor, hobbling toward my front door with a stack of Monopoly games and cans of Pork 'n' Beans he'd stashed for almost sixty years, yelling in his reedy voice "The time has come! The time has come!"

Maybe I'm being bitter. Last time I "played" was when I was thirteen in my school Monopoly tournament. Can you believe it, a *tournament?*

I was kicked off the team because after ten minutes of playing, I decided that amassing large numbers of railroad stations was no way to vanquish an opposition. Recalling the techniques of the Luftwaffe in World War II, I prepared to dive-bomb everyone's little plastic houses and hotels with my pewter top hat.

Heid the Ball, the kid who slept at the desk next to mine in studyhall, complained that top hats couldn't dive-bomb.

"Oh, yeah? Watch this!" I said and wiped out Paddington Station (we were playing the British version).

Although *blitzkreiging* the opposition out of existence made perfect sense to me, I quickly discovered it was Against The Rules. Another demerit to add to my collection, which I decided was now my new hobby . . .

Meanwhile, as the tournament continued, I entertained myself by trying to electrocute a bunch of zucchini's I'd looted from the school kitchen, an experiment which didn't go over real well, what with all the slimy green stuff plastered to the pristine white tiled kitchen walls.

The school sent a letter to my parents expressing great concern about my pyromaniac tendencies, worrying my mother for months. She'd prayed to St. Jude (Patron Saint of Hopeless Cases) that I'd stop getting in trouble but apparently Jude had turned a deaf ear.

Dad, on the other hand, said he was proud of my inquisitive mind! What a guy—my grades were terrible, but I sure knew how to blow up things!

During all those years of social struggles, no one had ever pointed out that perhaps I was doing something wrong. Of course, if they had, I'm sure I'd have blown them off, but I can't help but wonder if it would have made a difference.

Recently, I mentioned to a kid just like Travis the Social Skills King, that he was like a human tornado the way he crashed into rooms, invaded people's space, and spoke too loud. Although he was almost fourteen-years-old, no one had ever told him what he was like directly. His family had always skirted the issue and danced around the sidelines, not wanting to upset or embarrass him. While their intentions were noble, it didn't help their kid much!

When I told him, he was angry and hurt, but he began to see why he had such a hard time keeping friends.

His parents had been worried for years, but fretting and worrying won't do anything to change the situation. You need to be honest. Naturally, that doesn't mean saying, "Hey, Junior! Your social skills stink!" but it does mean pointing out where you see him going wrong, and explaining why other kids react the way they do.

Who knows, one day your ADHD kid might host his own TV talk show because of his most excellent social skills!

Chapter 14

The Three R'S:
Readin', Ritin', and Ritalin

What ADHD book would be complete without discussing the controversies about ADHD medication?

Initially, I wanted to do an overview of medication, especially Ritalin, but then realized that as a non-medical person, I wasn't particularly comfortable spouting off authoritatively about what medication does and doesn't do. I'll leave that to the experts, the biochemists, doctors, and pharmacists, who know far more than I do about the technical aspects of medication.

However, as someone who actually uses the stuff, specifically Ritalin, and doesn't just read about it or observe others using it in studies, I have some observations to make that may be of use to you as a parent.

A word of caution: the decision to use any medication is a serious one, a decision that must be made by discussing the pros and cons extensively with a knowledgeable physician *after a thorough evaluation and proper diagnosis.*

The very concept of ADHD itself is highly controversial in various circles, but this controversy can't hold a candle to the emotions, charges, and counter-charges about Ritalin. People wage war over this medication!

You think I'm exaggerating? Fine, log onto the Internet, search for "Ritalin," and see what you come up with:

7,000,000,000,000 "authoritatively-written" articles about why Ritalin is the Spawn of Satan!

My own search produced articles like, "Ritalin Destroyed my Child!" "The Evils of Ritalin and Other Government Conspiracies!" and "Ritalin Killed my Sex Life!" Additionally, many of these articles appear to have been written by the same author, who, incidentally, is selling an herbal alternative.

And you thought the Swiss only made cute. little cuckoo clocks and really good chocolate! (CIBA-GEIGY or whatever they're called now, the company who manufacture brand name Ritalin, is Swiss.)

Okay, so what *is* Ritalin anyway? It's the brand name of the drug *methylphenidate*, a mild stimulant. Like other stimulants, it appears to increase the amount of dopamine in the brain's frontal lobe, the area that governs impulsivity and attention span. When an ADHD kid takes Ritalin, the results include a decrease in impulsivity and an increase in concentration.

But it all depends on whom you ask. There are a number of docs who are terrified of the stuff due to old myths about it being a street drug, and also because of past criticisms launched against the medication by Scientology.

Others prescribe Ritalin like candy after meeting with a child for about fifteen minutes, adding fuel to the fire of controversy.

In 1996, there was a report released by the FDA claiming that Ritalin could cause a rare form of liver cancer (some of the data came from mouse studies). The media went haywire splashing scary headlines all across the country. As a result, fearful parents started yanking the medication away from their kids despite there being no hard evidence that the same form of liver cancer was higher among Ritalin users, a fact based on decades-long studies on groups of users.

So the FDA stated that although it's not a good idea for mice, the research indicates that for people, Ritalin is still safe and effective.

So, not only do we have folks being for or against Ritalin, we now have government agencies that are both for *and* against it simultaneously. As one of my ADHD adult clients stated recently, "Yeah, Ritalin causes hepatoblastoma in mice, but I'm not a mouse, so what's the problem?"

See how this controversy can drive you crazy? Who do you believe?

You talk to a rival medication manufacturer, like the guys who make the new ADHD drug, Adderall, and they'll tell you that Ritalin is garbage, and unless you switch over to Adderall, you're screwed.

Talk with a Cylert (a non-stimulant ADHD medication) rep, and she'll tell you that Adderall is nothing more than a slick-marketed amphetamine cocktail no better than any other medication on the market, maybe even worse.

Listen to a Ritalin sales rep, and she'll tell you Ritalin is the medication of choice for winners, the breakfast of champions! (*Breakfast of Champions* is also a book by Kurt Vonnegut.)

So what's a confused parent to do? Not only do the FDA and the media make conflicting statements, so do the sales reps, the docs, the pharmacists, and even the kids themselves!

What you do is learn what's what. Talk to professionals you trust. Read articles written from both sides of the issues, but not by the traveling-medicine show salespersons who are currently flooding the Internet and certain magazines about how dangerous Ritalin is and how you should buy *their* non-medical product instead! Talk to other moms and dads whose kids have used ADHD medications.

If having done all this (and you're still sane), you now need to make a decision about whether or not to go ahead. Again, I emphasize the importance of consultation with a medical doctor you trust. And remember, your kid has some say, too. You can't just say, "Okay, Johnny, we're gonna start drugging you up to make you calm down and do better in school."

Make sure he understands what it's all about. If you do decide to go ahead, remember too, that it's not a life sentence (which is impossible because legally, you can only get a month's supply at a time due to Ritalin being a controlled substance. But that's a whole other story.)

Finding the right dose is critical. If it's too high, your kid might have stomach upsets, insomnia, facial tics or start biting his nails. If it's too low, you might not see any difference whatsoever.

Or maybe it just doesn't work, which happens in about 20 percent of cases, according to Dr. Ned Hallowell. Yet maybe Cylert, Dexedrine, or Adderall works instead. Or Wellbutrin, a type of anti-depressant that works very well for a number of ADHD kids.

The bottom line is that everyone is different, with differing metabolisms, tolerances, and physiologies.

But the fact remains that when a sixteen-year-old boy is sitting across from me with tears running down his face saying, "Why couldn't I have found this years ago?" because he's been on Ritalin a couple of weeks and his whole life seems to be turning around, well, that sure gets my attention. Not the first time that's happened, either.

Don't get me wrong, ADHD medication of any kind is not a magic bullet. It's not the Holy Grail, nor the Great Cure-All. With or without medication, ADHD takes a lot of work and effort to conquer. Medication is only one piece of the puzzle and it's not for everyone.

These aren't "smart pills" nor are they "happy pills." They are medications that have helped countless kids and adults with ADHD, that's all.

Here are some comments from kids and adults I know who have used medication successfully:

C.B., a 20-year old white male: "When I don't use Ritalin, I feel like my mind is a pebble skimming across the surface of a pond. I land on the surface for a second or less, then I'm skimming on to the next portion of water, on and on, around in circles, never stopping. Then I get "Sewing Machine Leg," like I can't stop bouncing it up and down."

V.T., a 13-year old African-American male: "ADHD means you're hyper. Your friends think you're kind of crazy and you can't sit still and your teacher's always yelling at you because you talk too much and you don't even *know* you're talking. Adderall makes you shut your big mouth."

H.M., an 18-year old white female: "ADHD without Dexedrine is like I have a VCR in my head. As soon as I feel bored, the VCR switches on and plays a movie. Then you don't like what you're watching, so you change who the main character is. The guy she's falling for is a real creep, so you have to kill him off. The movie goes on and on until you hear your teacher calling your name and you feel, like, so dumb!

But it's like you can't control it even if you try. Dexedrine is the OFF button for my VCR."

H.R., a 39-year old white male: "What's it like in my head without Ritalin? Trust me, you don't want to know. Okay, you asked, so maybe you do. Right, I'm in a meeting at work, an important meeting in which salaries and bonuses are discussed. I really want to know what's going on because the outcome of this meeting affects me directly. But here's what I do after about five minutes; I start doodling circles in my notebook. Nancy sitting beside me has a run in her pantyhose. Looks like a tiny ladder. That's why they call it a ladder. Why do women call it a run? It doesn't go anywhere. God, I'd love to go somewhere. I need a vacation. Hawaii. Never been to Hawaii. Fresh pineapple sounds good. Damn, I forgot to have breakfast. Damn, I forgot my meds as well, no wonder my thoughts are all over the place. I'm hungry. Could use a bagel right now. Billy's Bagels, saw that new place on the way here this morning. New company. Oh, man! Sheila said we're having company tonight. What was it she asked me to pick up . . . darn it, can't remember. If I call her, she'll be mad. Is that a blue jay on the windowsill out there? Nope, it's a skinny pigeon. You don't really see blue jays around office blocks like this. Lots of Canadian geese, though. Flying south for winter. To Florida. Florida would be cheaper than Hawaii.

"Then I hear my boss saying, 'Harry, what do you think of Ben's proposal?' and I want to curl up under the conference table and disappear because I've just made an idiot of myself by zoning out."

So not everyone who uses Ritalin or other ADHD medications has horror stories. If you're scared of the horror stories, don't use the medication!

I'll be the first to admit, I was scared to use it myself, having read every horror story ever published. But I had also read numerous success stories, and most importantly, I'd seen countless positive results in others.

The first time I ever used Ritalin was several years ago. Although I'd learned tons of compensatory behavior, and had adapted quite well to being an ADHD'er (of course, that all depends on whom you talk with), I was aware that my ways of doing things were still very difficult, and downright exhausting on occasion.

With a growing sense of anxiety, I took one 20mg Ritalin SR (Sustained Release), having discussed the pros and cons with my doc for the umpteenth time. I then sat down at my computer, and began to write.

After about forty minutes, I was suddenly aware of a dramatic silence inside my head, a silence that was almost eerie. I listened intently, puzzled by the acute lack of noise. Then it hit me; my head was always full of static, filled with thousands of thoughts, ideas, and possibilities, which created a barrage of background noise. I'd become so used to it, I thought it was normal, that everyone had this racket going on inside them.

Try to imagine you have a TV, a CD player, and a radio inside your head, all playing at the same time and the radio switches channels every few seconds all by itself. Although it's distracting as hell, you've no other choice but to live with it. Then suddenly, someone comes along and turns them all off at the same time!

In the deep silence, I glanced up at the computer screen and read the manuscript page I'd just typed. I read it slowly and immediately caught all the typos that had slipped by, despite the fact I'd supposedly proofread the page at least twice.

When I wrote in longhand, even the speed at which I wrote slowed down, so much so, that I actually laughed out loud as it seemed to take forever. Fascinated with all these instant changes, I left for work, listening to the car radio. A bigger surprise awaited me—I stayed with the one radio station throughout the journey to my office, instead of scanning all the stations every two seconds, my usual habit.

But did my wonderment stop here? No! The best was yet to come, in the songs themselves. For the first time in my life, I finally heard all the words to a song!

I'm a relatively musical person (although I had always refused to read sheet music because it looked so mathematical) and I can fumble my way around a guitar, and a few other instruments. I play by ear and know plenty of tunes, picking up new melodies easily, yet I'll be damned if I can ever remember the words to the tunes!

The only two songs I know the words to are "Happy Birthday," and the US national anthem, which I had to learn when I became a US citizen.

Driving to work that day, I was flooded with lyrics from the radio. Hearing all the words was like entering a whole new world.

Another instant side effect was a noticeable decrease in anxiety, which like the internal static in my head, I'd gotten used to. Much of the anxiety came from procrastinating about paperwork, not making phone calls, and not quite meeting deadlines.

Over the years, I'd worked at becoming relatively organized, using a filing system and an appointment book,
which I opened most of the time, but not always. Even
though it was sitting in front of me, it just seemed to blend
into the background and disappear.

When I started using Ritalin, not only did the appointment book materialize, I actually wrote in it every day and
read it. I also discovered if I made entries in red ink, I'd pay
even more attention.

But the greatest system I ever found was one of those
little electronic CASIO BOSS organizers because any time I
was bored in meetings, I could play with the keys.

But with Ritalin, playing around with the keys became *so*
focused. I learned that if I turned the calculator part upside
down, and punched in the numbers 738051, they spelled out
my little sister's name, "Isobel." Or that 0553 reads as
"EGGO" and 0537 reads as "LEGO." See, there's no end to
the possibilities when your mind wanders and you have a
Ritalin and a CASIO.

Where was I? Oh, yes, a decrease in anxiety. There was
also a dramatic decrease in my procrastination. My sixth
grade teacher had always told me, "Procrastination is the thief
of time." Was that ever an understatement or what!

Using Ritalin seemed to remove my life-long career of
procrastination, and I'd find myself cleaning closets, the ga-
rage, and generally following through on boring, repetitive
tasks at an incredible rate.

Types of Ritalin

There are two main types of Ritalin, the regular, which
lasts about four hours, then wears off rapidly, and the time-

released version, Ritalin SR (Sustained Release). When the regular type wears off, many kids complain about a "crash," that they feel it suddenly leaving their system. As Derek, a sixteen-year-old explains, "One minute you're focused, taking notes in class, next minute it's like you've been hit by a truck. Your mind wanders, the class material starts to seem distant, and when you read, nothing makes sense until you read it twenty times over."

There's also the problem of forgetting to take it. Let's say your kid takes 10 mg three times a day. First one is at 7:00 A.M, second at 11:00 A.M., and third at 3:00 P.M. That's fine for school but what about when he comes home? So often, parents complain that as soon as their kid walks through the door at the end of the day, all hell breaks loose because he's just used up his last dose of medication.

There are two possible solutions to this one. The first is take a smaller dose when he gets home, and the second is to switch him over to Ritalin SR. Incidentally, *you* can't switch him over, only the prescribing physician can do that.

Officially, Ritalin SR is supposed to last between six to eight hours, but the reality is that it depends on the person's physiology, how much food is in their stomach when they take it, and so on. Some kids and adults experience wonderful results with Ritalin SR, including myself, but for others, the release can be inconsistent, as in the case of Mikey:

Mikey had one of the most severe cases of ADHD PIT I'd ever seen. Without medication, you'd swear he was dead or at least had passed out. He'd just sit there, a fog over his eyes, over his entire mind.

With the regular Ritalin, he did very well personally and academically, making the honor roll several times. Life was good for Mikey.

Then around his sixteenth birthday, his doctor decided to switch him over to Ritalin SR, as he believed this to be more appropriate with older kids.

Mikey said, "Sure, if you think it's best."

On the third day of Mikey taking the Ritalin SR, Mom decided to go shopping, leaving Mikey to mow the lawn. When she came home, she stopped dead at the sight of her two prize shrubs having been stuffed into the trash, followed by the sight of Mikey going after a third with a hacksaw.

She ran up to him. "Mikey, what in God's name are you doing? My shrubs!"

He shrugged. "Didn't you tell me to chop them down?"

"What? Are you crazy? No! I only told you to mow the lawn, for goodness sake!"

Mikey shook his head. "Man, I could've sworn I heard you tell me to prune the shrubs. Yeah, you did. I heard you telling Aunt Kathy you needed to trim the bushes, that they were too big and that I should help you because I don't show enough initiative and here's my big chance and how about if I wash your car, maybe even change the oil, I know how to do it because I have a book that shows you and then . . ."

Mikey was talking faster and faster, then he crashed, a blank look crossing his face, the way he used to look before he ever went on medication.

Mom was puzzled. Mikey hadn't acted like this since his pre-Ritalin days . . .

But it didn't stop there. The following morning, she was awoken by a loud, buzzing sound. Jumping out of bed, she followed the sound down to the basement where she found Mikey standing in a cloud of white dust. "What are you *doing?*" she yelled.

Waving her hand through the dust cloud, she found him hovering over a mahogany coffee table wielding a power sander. The top of the table had been completely sanded away. "My God! What are you *doing?*"

Mikey laid the sander down. "You said I don't show enough initiative and I was lying under the table this morning thinking about what that meant and I noticed there were scratches on the table top and I know how much you like this table so I thought I'd strip it for you and refinish it and you'd be pleased and then you'd not be so upset about the shrubs and then . . ." He turned around and winked at the TV cabinet. "And then, well, the TV could use some work too, and once I finish that. . ."

Controlling her panic, Mom scheduled an emergency appointment with the doctor. After considerable investigation, the doctor concluded that Mikey's body seemed to use up all six to eight hour's worth of Ritalin during the first hour or so of administration, then metabolize out of his system, causing him to "crash."

When the doctor put him back on regular Ritalin, Mikey quickly returned to normal.

This is one of the criticisms leveled at the sustained release version, and even the regular to some extent, that the release can be unpredictable. Yet it all depends on the individual concerned, the age of the child, his physiology, and a host of other factors. That's why the medication decision should not be rushed.

To make an informed medication decision, you need to discuss the options thoroughly with your physician. I know I've already said that, but I'm saying it again to get the point across.

The bottom line is that ADHD medications are not a panacea for everything and anything.

A word of caution: If you kid does start using medication, don't get into the habit of attributing all of his unacceptable behavior to the medication or lack thereof, and make comments like:

"Have you taken your Ritalin?"
"Do you need an extra pill or something?"
"Here, moron, take another anti-hyper pill."
"I won't talk to you until you've taken your medicine."

It's obvious why some kids are against the whole idea of medication because these kinds of comments and questions make them feel like freaks.

But the best of all is when our fourteen-year-old daughter asks me the same kinds of questions. That really does wonders for my self-esteem as a parental unit. There she is wearing baggy pants wide enough to take flight in a high wind, a fluorescent lime green shirt someone left in a dumpster in 1968, a peace symbol hanging from her neck, while she tries to keep her balance on her, like, really cool 27-inch platform shoes, listening to music that makes your ears bleed. And she has the nerve to ask me if *I'm* on medication!

Of course, I always wreak sweet revenge. When I drop her off at school, I wind down the car window and yell at the top of my lungs, "Expand your horizons! Learn new things! Education is the key to your future!" right in front of her, like, really cool friends. That took care of her asking me if I was using Ritalin. She never asked again.

As an adult who uses Ritalin, there's no question in my mind that it helps tremendously. Does it change who I am or change my personality? Nope, but it does make me more focused and more organized.

A concern I often hear from parents and the kids themselves is that medication might somehow decrease creativity. In my own case, I've found that Ritalin enhances my creativity, because instead of working on ten manuscripts at different stages of development, I remain with one until it's completed all the way through. In other words, my creativity isn't diminished, it's now focused. Hence this book, now that I think about it.

So if you're thinking about medication, get all the facts first, and talk with people who know and can discuss the subject from both sides of the coin. Only when you have all the facts can you make an informed decision.

Conclusion

So there you have it, homework-eating wildebeest and all. I told you at the start of this book that it wasn't going to be a scholarly or academic work, and I've been true to my word, it wasn't.

Even so, I do hope I've been able to shed some light on this complicated, perplexing, paradoxical condition, and on occasion, have maybe even entertained you.

My final comment is that having a kid with ADHD doesn't need to be the end of the world. Remember, the only thing that's the end of the world is the end of the world, and this ain't it—at least, not yet.

There is hope. There really is light at the end of the tunnel, and hopefully, you'll find some peace and quiet both in your heart and in your family.

God Bless you on your journey.

Tom Quinn
Sutherland & Associates
600 Emerson, Ste. 218
Creve Coeur, MO 63141

(314) 692 0880
email:tquinn@primary.net

References

American Psychiatric Association, 1994. *Diagnostic and Statistical Manual of Psychiatric Disorders,* 4th Ed. Washington, DC.

Barkley, R.A., 1990. *Attention Deficit Hyperactivity Disorder,* New York, Guilford.

Goldstein, S., 1997. *Managing Attention and Learning Disorders in Late Adolescence & Adulthood,* New York, John Wiley & Sons, Inc.

Hallowell, E.M., & Ratey, J.J, 1994. *Driven to Distraction,* New York, Pantheon.

Panati, C, 1987. *Extraordinary Origins of Everyday Things,* New York, Harper & Row.

Pennington, B.F., 1991. *Diagnosing Learning Disorders,* New York, Guilford.

Quinn, T.G., 1996-7, *The St. Louis ADD Newsletter,* St. Louis.

Smith, S., 1991. *Succeeding Against the Odds,* New York, Putnam.

A

academic accommodations, 169
ADD, 11
  Disorder Formerly Known As, 12
  female type, 21, 22
Adderall, 70, 155, 245, 246, 247
ADHD myths, 153, 155
ADHD: Combined Type (CT), 13, 26
ADHD: Hyperactive-Impulsive Type (HIT), 13, 16
ADHD: Not Otherwise Specified (NOS), 13, 30
ADHD: Predominantly Inattentive Type, 13, 21
alcoholism
  family history of, 67, 73
  relationship to ADHD, 156
Amateur Psychology:101, 174
American Speech-Language-Hearing Association
  CAPD definition and the, 51
anxiety, 47, 48, 49, 51, 57, 96, 114, 188, 189, 249, 250, 251
  parental, 96
  symptoms of, 47, 49
Anxiety
  ADHD, differences between disorders, 48
  Generalized Anxiety Disorder and, 48

parental and teachers, 188
appetite
  poor, dysthymia, symptom of, 50
appointment book
  organizational tool, 87, 251
Attention Deficit Hyperactivity Disorder, 13

B

Baby Steps, 88
basket case, 116
Blessed Martyr, 108
  Mom role of, 95, 106
Blue-Green Algae, 12
bootstraps, 160, 161
  pulling self up by, 160
boredom
  low tolerance for, 21, 38, 190
  reason for lying, 35, 40
  teachers in, 191
brain
  ADHD, 75
  frontal areas of, 76
  frontal lobe and, 244
  metabolism, 32, 33, 159
  metabolism studies, 75

C

caffeine, 33
CAPD
  definition of, 51

Tom Quinn has worked with adolescents since 1980, when he was a social worker in his native Glasgow, Scotland. He continued his career in St. Louis, Missouri, earning a Master's Degree in Counseling from Webster University. From 1993-96 he was an Adjunct Faculty member of St. Louis Community College at Meramec where he taught Adolescent Psychology, Abnormal Psychology and Alcohol and Drug Studies.

As an ADHD adult himself, Quinn draws upon his own experience, giving the reader an "insider's view," making use of straightforward, creative behavioral management techniques along with a keen sense of humor.

An entertaining speaker and workshop presenter, Quinn is also the publisher and editor of the *St. Louis ADHD Newsletter.*

Quinn has been in private practice since 1989. His private practice is at Sutherland & Associates, 600 Emerson, Ste. 218, Creve Coeur, Missouri 63141, (314) 692-0880.

ORDER FORM

☎ Telephone orders: Call Toll Free: **1-800-871-0803**
 We accept Visa, Mastercard and Discover

① Fax orders: **(314) 692 0514**

✉ Mail orders: Dunvegan Publishing, Inc.
  1170 Keystone Trail Drive,
  Wildwood, MO 63005

▱ Website: Secure ordering at:

http://www.adhdcounselorguy.com

Grandma's Pet Wildebeest Ate My Homework: $16.95

Name: _____

Address: _____

City: _____ State: _____ Zip: _____

Telephone: (___) _____

Payment:
❑ Check
❑ Credit card: VISA, MasterCard, Discover (please circle)

Card number:_____

Name on card: _____ Exp.date: ____/_____

Book	Quantity	Price	Total
		Sub total	
	Add $1.01 tax for Missouri residents		
	Shipping & Handling $5.95 plus $2.00 for each additional book		
		Total